THE ROYAL SOCIETY

TERCENTENARY

PRINTED IN ENGLAND
BY HARRISON AND SONS LIMITED
BY APPOINTMENT TO HER MAJESTY THE QUEEN,
PRINTERS, LONDON, HAYES (MIDDX.) AND HIGH WYCOMBE

THE
ROYAL SOCIETY
TERCENTENARY

compiled from a

special supplement of

THE TIMES

JULY, 1960

LONDON

THE TIMES PUBLISHING COMPANY LIMITED

PRINTING HOUSE SQUARE

1961

CONTENTS

Sir Isaac Newton (1703–1727)

Lord Brouncker (1662–1667)

FAMOUS PRESIDENTS

Sir Joseph Banks (1778–1820)

Sir Christopher Wren (1680–1682)

Thomas Henry Huxley (1883–1885)

Sir Humphry Davy (1820–1827)

FAMOUS PRESIDENTS

Lord Lister (1895-1900)

Lord Kelvin (1890–1895)

Sir Cyril Hinshelwood (1955–1960)

Lord Rutherford (1925–1930)

Gresham College, original home of the Royal Society from 1660 to 1666, and later from 1673 to 1710.   Here chairs of geometry and astronomy were established for the first time in England.

Scala pedum.

References to places in the College.

1 . Gate into Bishopsgate street.
2 . Court within the gate.
3 . Physic prof. lodgings.
4 . Reading hall.
5 . Music prof. lodgings.
      Porters rooms underneath.
6 . Passage between the two courts.
7 . Green court.
8 . Observatory.
9 . Geometry prof. lodgings.
10 . { Back door into the geometry
      { prof. lodgings.
11 . Room behind the reading hall.
12 . Divinity prof. lodgings.
13 . Physic prof. elaboratory.
14 . Back door to the elaboratory.
15 . Rhetoric prof. lodgings.

16 . { Door into the rhetoric p
      { lodgings.
17 . North piazza.
18 . Astronomy prof. lodging
19 . South or long gallery.
20 . South piazza.
21 . { Fore door into the astro
      { prof. lodgings.
22 . West or white gallery.
23 . Almes houses.
24 . West end of the south ga
25 . Gate into the stable yard
26 . Law prof. lodgings.
27 . { Fore door into the law p
      { lodgings.
28 . Passage into Sun yard.
29 . Stable yard and stables.

The Council

Left to right: Prof. J. Z. Young, Prof. R. J. Pumphrey, Prof. D. G. Catcheside, Prof. T. M. Harris, Prof. L. Hawkes, Dr. D. C. Martin (Asst. Secy.), Mr. W. M. Malcolm (Clerk of Council), Sir William Penney, Sir Lindor Brown, Sir Cyril Hinshelwood, Sir William Hodge, Sir Gerard Thornton, Dr. J. C. Burkill, Dr. R. A. Lyttleton, Dame Kathleen Lonsdale, Sir Alfred Pugsley, Dr. H. W. Thompson, Prof. R. A. Morton, Prof. A. L. Hodgkin. Sir Patrick Linstead, Prof. W. Smith, Prof. J. F. Baker, and Sir Harrie Massey were unable to be present.

STATUS FOR THE MODERN AGE

THE tercentenary of the Royal Society compels attention regardless of country, politics, or interest in the old for its own sake. The Society is the centre and focus of science in Britain. For its Fellows it is a living fact, not " one of history ", that a king—Charles II —ranks as its founder. A portrait of him by SIR PETER LELY looks down on its Fellows at their every meeting; the mace that he presented is still in use; the Charter Book, in which all fellows have signed in unbroken succession for 300 years, was also his gift. But it is not for its origins that the Society receives as host representatives of national academies and universities throughout the world. Neither is it because the Society—although founded three years later than the original Italian Academia del Cimento—is the oldest scientific society or organised scientific academy that has enjoyed continuouse xistence from its foundation onwards, though there is cause for pride in this fact. Neither, again, is it for

the talent that its founders brought together or because it had the honour of electing ISAAC NEWTON first to the Fellowship and later as President. No society, any more than a country, can live on its past.

What, then, makes the celebrations both an international and a national occasion? First, there has been no period in the past when science has had more effect on men's lives and thoughts, or when it has been more important that the facts and theories to which it leads should be critically discussed and presented. There can be no official view in science. The Society, according to its motto, is bound to no master's words, and neither are its Fellows. This independence, which 300 years ago marked a breaking-free from Aristotle and the masters of antiquity, can be taken today to mean independence from set orthodoxies, preconceived philosophies, and prejudice deriving from day-to-day policy. The claim of the Society to respect under this heading is

11

that it has entered the modern age with a scientific status and a reputation for integrity that are without comparison.

Secondly, the Society has been international in its interests from the beginning, and has been so recognized. It has survived in turn the American War of Independence, the Napoleonic wars, two World Wars, and a period of tension in relations with Russia without damage to its relations with overseas scientists. Perhaps the nicest incident in its history is the fact that SIR HUMPHRY DAVY, when President, should have been given permission by NAPOLEON to travel in Europe at a time when France and England were at war and the toast of the Society drunk in Paris in his honour. Such traditions and such a reputation are worth much in an age in which the world—self-sufficient and self-explanatory in itself—is apt to be divided by adjectives placed in front of it.

Thirdly, international cooperation in research leans more heavily on organization than ever before. Whether the subject is space, oceanography, or questions of units and symbols, there is an advantage and influence in promoting agreement from the existence of a national body of scientists whose tradition is to consider issues on their merits. Without claiming more for the Society than its due, this has been the reputation won by its representatives on international bodies—regardless of the issue discussed.

Participation by both the QUEEN and the DUKE OF EDINBURGH in the celebrations is from one point of view, a matter domestic to the Society. The one is Patron, the other a Fellow; and the Society is royal by Charter. But there is another, more constitutional, way of looking at the matter. Whereas various other countries have national academies in the sense that the state is responsible for them, the Royal Society has been an independent organization from the beginning. It is in touch with government departments, both in its own right and through various of its Fellows. But it is not of them—and in that fact there lies much of the strength of the Society. It is a means by which opinion can be brought to bear, and it acts also as a non-official purveyor of research grants. In conditions in which the greater part of the funds needed for research come directly or indirectly from the Treasury, this is an already useful safeguard—and it is likely to grow in importance. In this sense it may be said that the Society is necessary to the state, but is not responsible to it; and in the peculiar British way of doing things the cloak of royalty is then appropriate.

Finally, the tercentenary has provided an occasion for the Society to place science in Britain on view, primarily for its visitors for their interest, but also indirectly for the public. In these and other ways the celebrations provide a reminder of the great part in discovery that has been played—and is still being played—by British scientists.

12

The spirit of inquiry is international, an attribute of man, not of nations. Yet some show of pride is permissible, and it is no more than politeness in a host to open the treasures of his house to visitors. Some idea of their extent can be gathered from various contributions to this book, many of them by Fellows of the Society. They stand not in isolation, but as part of the extending fabric of science, a consequence of curiosity applied with discipline, and an assurance that, if man could indeed know himself, to make the world better would be easy.

IMPROVEMENT OF NATURAL KNOWLEDGE

By Sir Cyril Hinshelwood, O.M., F.R.S.
President of the Royal Society

KING CHARLES II constituted himself the founder of the Royal Society and by this act not only demonstrated his personal sympathy with the philosophic labours of a group of learned men, but expressed his belief that their activities would in one way or another bring advantage to his realm, and to the world.

According to any sane assessment the faith of 1660 has been fulfilled, and in the Tercentenary celebrations we pay tribute not only to the foundation members but to all those through the three centuries who in peace or in strife, in brilliance or in obscurity, have brought the sciences to where they stand today, who have applied them to the useful arts and have created the foundations of industry.

The Tercentenary can justly be regarded as an event in which the whole world shares, not only because the Royal Society is the scientific academy with the longest

continuous existence, but because its own membership and traditions have had a strongly international character. The present fellows are drawn from all parts of the British Commonwealth, and the list of its Foreign Members includes many of the greatest names, past and present, among the men of science of all nations. The common pursuit of truth is something which has endured the stresses of by-gone wars and transcended modern ideologies. It can penetrate the barriers of political misunderstanding.

The Society is very happy indeed on this present occasion to welcome so many guests and so many of its foreign members and fellows from overseas. It takes pride in being the principal link between the United Kingdom and the various international unions whose collective work, recently exemplified in the International Geophysical Year, assumes greater importance as time passes. It is glad to be the

The Copley Medal. Above, obverse and reverse of the original medal; below, the one in use at present. Apart from the Presidency, this award is the greatest honour the Society can confer. It was inaugurated by a £100 legacy from Sir Godfrey Copley in 1709.

vehicle of personal exchanges with various countries, an activity which it hopes to expand in the interests of promoting human welfare.

The Charter of the Society rests on the assumption that knowledge of the workings of nature provides a sure foundation for the development of what we now call technology. Discovery, analysis, invention and application are activities between which no definite boundaries can be set, and certainly none is recognized by the Royal Society, which numbers on its roll scholars of the most varied interests, together with practical men of widely different kinds.

The central aim of its existence is still the "improvement, of natural knowledge", and it is in pursuit of this major end that it fosters international understanding and encourages the union of thought with action. In this general sense there can justly be said to be a policy of the Society. As a body it does intervene directly in these matters in its appointments to research professorships, fellowships and studentships, in its administration of research funds, in the sponsoring of expeditions, in its conduct of relations with the international unions, and in its service to the Crown in governing the Royal Observatory and the National Physical Laboratory.

But in detail the activity of the Society is the sum total of the activities of its individual fellows, who are chosen with care

and impartiality and belong to no single school of thought. Their views may differ, and there is room both for rebels and conformists in a body which collectively asserts in its motto, *Nullius in Verba*, that it is bound in obedience to none.

The place of science in the community has greatly changed in the course of three centuries, and that of the Royal Society has changed with it. In the early days of the foundation there were no professional men of science. All were in a sense amateurs, though they ranged from men of scientific genius like Boyle and Newton to men like Pepys who were probably innocent of much profound knowledge of nature but wished the savants well, and believed generally in the potentialities of the new philosophy.

Throughout the centuries men endowed with genius or possessing the temperament to dedicate themselves occurred with varying frequency, but in the eighteenth and early nineteenth centuries the general body of the fellowship became diluted with a number of people who were at best dilettanti or who regarded themselves as members of an exclusive club. This state of affairs was transformed by the great developments of the mid-nineteenth century and the growth of the scientific professions. Election became restricted to a fixed annual number, and was made subject to stringent demands, the general effect of which was to make the Royal Society the gathering ground of scientic leaders.

16

At present, of the 25 annual elections of fellows, the great majority are made in virtue of outstanding direct contributions to the advance of knowledge, but a few of the places are filled by persons whose contribution has consisted more in their leadership, inspiration, and application of scientific investigation than in their personal research work. Under a special statute, rare elections (not exceeding one a year) take place of persons who have rendered " conspicuous service to the cause of science ". The Duke of Edinburgh and King Gustav of Sweden are fellows under this statute.

The vast complication of modern life, the expansion of industry, the growth of flourishing societies devoted to the separate branches of science, the increased expenditure by government departments on scientific projects, all mean that the influence of the Royal Society can be exercised less directly than it was when, for example, Queen Anne placed the Royal Observatory in its charge, or when it was invited just before the turn of the century to assume responsibility for the National Physical Laboratory. Though certain direct encroachments on its traditional functions are properly resisted, some changes are inevitable.

Though it has many corporate activities, today the Royal Society really exerts its most important influences through its individual fellows. So long as these are properly chosen and continue to include leaders from all branches of pure and applied science, the position of the Society in the scheme of things will remain unassailable.

BY ROYAL FAVOUR

THOUGH the Royal Society offici-
ally dates its foundation from July
15, 1662, it has a long pre-history,
institutionally in the Elizabethan Gresham
College, intellectually in the new conception of experimental philosophy inaugurated by Francis Bacon. Men attracted by
this outlook were meeting to exchange
ideas under the first two Stuarts; their
interest in the natural sciences became
more concentrated during the interregnum,
for there was little else to discuss. They
were refugees from the tumult of the time
when the grim Puritan repression made free
discussion of either politics or theology
dangerous.

Thus men of speculative mind took to
meeting in what one of the greatest of
them, Robert Boyle, called " the invisible
college ", of which their first historian,
Thomas Sprat, afterwards Bishop of
Rochester, wrote in 1667 that " their first
purpose was no more than only the
satisfaction of breathing a purer air, and of
conversing in quiet one with another,
without being ingag'd in the passions and
madness of that dismal age ". With the
death of Oliver Cromwell in 1658 and

the collapse of the Protectorate into anarchy,
the passions and madness grew so intolerable
that the quiet meetings of the learned men
had to be suspended; so that it is in truth
by virtue only of the Restoration of King
and Parliament, and the return of ordered
government, that they have been enabled
to bequeath a name to posterity. By the
end of November, 1660, they were meeting
again at Gresham College " to heare Master
Wren's lecture ", and agreeing to form
themselves into a permanent society,
meeting every Wednesday afternoon.

They were no doubt already aware that
the returned King desired to rival his
cousin Louis XIV as a patron of the arts
and sciences; and they had among them
one member, Sir Robert Moray, who was
known to be *persona grata* with his Majesty.
At the first meeting in December " Sir
Robert Moray brought in word from the
Court, that the King has been acquainted
with the designe of this Meeting. And
he did well approve of it, and would be
ready to give encouragement to it ".
So definite was this encouragement that
John Evelyn, himself one of the invisible
college, in a dedication to Clarendon, the

Lord Chancellor, in 1661, was already praising him for "the promoting and encouraging of the Royal Society".

In September a petition for incorporation was presented, and on October 16 Moray reported that "hee and Sr Paul Neile kiss'd the King's hands in the Company's Name . . . and to this favour and honour hee [the King] was pleased to offer of him selfe to bee enter'd one of the Society ". The charter of incorporation, as has been said, passed the Great Seal the following July. The Duke of York, Prince Rupert Duke of Cumberland, and Prince George, the husband of Princess Anne, were soon added to the list of royal fellows; and a further mark of favour was the grant of the arms: silver, with a quarter of England.

Charles continued to take a close personal interest in the work of the society, as Sprat puts it:

"When the *Society* first address'd themselves to his *Majestie*, he was pleas'd to express much satisfaction, that this enterprize was begun in *his Reign*: he then represented to them, the gravity, and difficulty of their work, and assur'd them of all the kind influence of his *Power*, and *Prerogative*. Since that he has frequently committed many things to their *search*: he has referr'd many forein *Rarities* to their *inspection*: he has recommended many domestick *improvements* to their care: he has demanded the result of their *trials*, in many appearances of *Nature*: he has been present, and assisted with his own hands, at the performing of many of their *Experiments*, in his *Gardens*, his *Parks*, and on the *River*. And besides I will not conceal, that he has sometimes reprov'd them for the *slowness* of their *proceedings*. at which reproofs they have not so much cause to be afflicted, that they are the reprehensions of a *King*, as to be comforted, that they are the reprehensions of his *love*, and *affection* to their progress."

A reverberation room in the laboratory, where reflecting plates are used to obtain uniformity in sound distribution.

HOME OF PHYSICS RESEARCH

The National Physical Laboratory at Teddington, Middlesex, was started by the Royal Society at the turn of the century, and today does valuable research in the fields of science and engineering.

Bushy House, original home of the National Physical Laboratory.

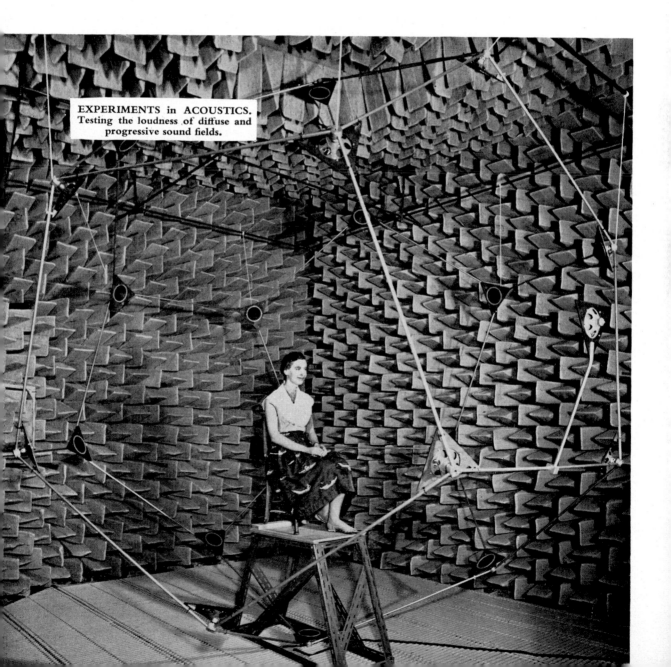

EXPERIMENTS in ACOUSTICS.
Testing the loudness of diffuse and progressive sound fields.

ORGAN OF THE "NEW PHILOSOPHY"

By Douglas McKie

Professor of the History and Philosophy of Science, University College, London

THE Royal Society of London, although not then so entitled, was formally constituted a scientific society at Gresham College in the City of London on Wednesday, November 28, 1660. Its 12 founders, as the original journal book of the Society records, were "The Lord Brouncker, Mr. Boyle, Mr. Bruce [later Earl of Kincardine], Sir Robert Moray, Sir Paul Neile, Dr. Wilkins, Dr. Goddard, Dr. Petty, Mr. Ball, Mr. Rooke, Mr. Wren, Mr. Hill". They had met on that day, as had been their custom for some time, to hear the lecture given by the Gresham Professor of Astronomy, Christopher Wren, and afterwards to "withdrawe for mutuall converse"; they then resolved to improve their meetings, as the journal book states, "to a more regular way of debating things, & according to the Manner in other Countryes, where there were voluntary associations of men

into Academies for the advancement of various parts of learning, so they might doe something answerable here for the promoting of Experimentall Philosophy". It is the tercentenary of this historic foundation meeting that is now being celebrated.

The mention of the institution of scientific academies in other countries can refer only to Italy and France, where there had long been such associations, even before Francis Bacon's suggested academy, the "Solomon's house" of his *New Atlantis* (1627), which was later too often assumed to have been influential in the foundation of the Royal Society, much in the same way as Bacon's method of induction, expounded in his *Novum organum* (1620), has often been erroneously regarded as a factor in the rise of modern science.

If we ask what brought these men together for this purpose at this time and place, we must turn, first, to Western Europe, the birth-place of modern science, where the " new philosophy " of studying nature by experiment and observation had been gaining strength since the early part of the sixteenth century; and secondly, to that late Elizabethan foundation Gresham College, where a sound scientific tradition had been securely established since the closing years of that century.

The advance of the " new philosophy ", or science, as we now call it, in Western Europe is most conveniently recalled in this short space by reference to a few classics of its literature. Biringuccio's *De la pirotechnia* (1540) was the first printed work on general technology; Fuchs's *De historia stirpium* (1542) delineated plants accurately; Vesalius's *De humani corporis fabrica* (1543) derived its anatomy from dissections instead of ancient texts; Copernicus's *De revolutionibus orbium cœlestium* (1543) propounded a heliocentric instead of the accepted geocentric system of sun and planets; Galileo's *Siderius Nuncius* (1610) described the remarkable discoveries made with his newly devised telescope, that puny instrument with which in his day he almost immeasurably increased man's knowledge of the universe; his *Dialogo* (1632) refuted the ancient Ptolemaic system in favour of the Copernican, and his *Discorsi* (1638) expounded his work on mechanics; Descartes in his *Géométrie* (1637) applied algebraic methods to geometrical problems and thus put a new weapon into the hands of the scientist

and in his *Principia philosophiæ* (1644) he described in terms of his vortex theory a mechanical and corpuscular world system that carried scientific thought still farther away from the ancient authorities. The English contribution was outstanding: William Gilbert's treatise on the magnet and magnetic bodies, the *De magnete* (1600), the first classic of modern physical science, showed among other things that the Earth itself was a great magnet and satisfactorily explained the general facts of terrestrial magnetism and the behaviour of the compass-needle; and William Harvey's *De motu cordis* (1628) described his discovery of the circulation of the blood.

Meanwhile, in London, Gresham College had been opened in 1598 through the bequest of Sir Thomas Gresham, who had left his house in Bishopsgate Street as a college with endowments for seven resident professors. Here chairs of geometry and of astronomy were established for the first time in England. Among the early professors were Henry Briggs, who introduced common logarithms, Edmund Gunter, who carried on Brigg's work and also invented a number of instruments, including a simple form of the slide-rule, and Henry Gellibrand, who continued the studies of his predecessors. These men, as has been shown by Professor F. R. Johnson, were also closely associated in their scientific work with officers of the Royal Navy and naval administrators and shipbuilders. Moreover, Briggs was a friend of the

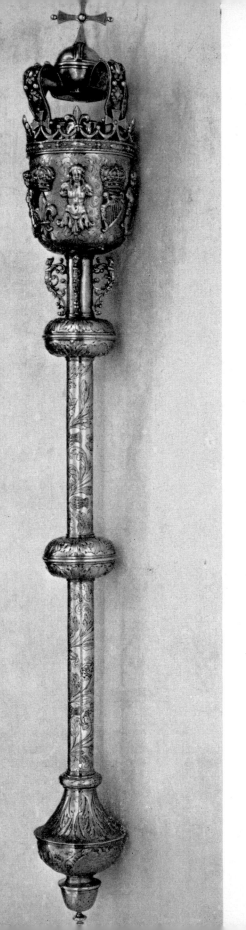

illustrious Gilbert and of Gilbert's friend's Edward Wright and Thomas Blundeville. Others were William Barlowe, Mark Ridley and Sir Thomas Challoner, and the famous mathematician William Oughtred. There was clearly in early seventeenth-century London an active scientific group associated with Gresham College. At the same time Harvey was in 1616 already expounding in his lectures at the College of Physicians his still unpublished discovery of the circulation of the blood.

About 1645 in Gresham College in term time or in some neighbouring place at other times, according to John Wallis, the first informal weekly meetings that ultimately led to the foundation of the Royal Society were held by a group that included, besides himself and some others, John Wilkins, Jonathan Goddard and Francis Glisson. These meetings may have been suggested by Theodore Haak, who corresponded with Mersenne, from whom he obtained what was probably the first news in England of the historic experiment of Torricelli disproving the belief in the impossibility of vacuum. Discussion was limited to scientific matters only, such as the circulation of the blood, the Copernican hypothesis, comets, stars and planets, the improvement of telescopes, the grinding of lenses, the weight of the air, the possibility

The Society's mace, presented by Charles II, is still placed before the President at each meeting.

Part of the first page of signatures in the Charter Book.

The Obligation of the Fellows of the ROYAL SOCIETY.

We who have hereunto subscribed, do hereby promise, each for himselfe, that we will endeavour to promote the Good of the Royall Society of London for impreving Naturall Knowledge; and to pursue the Ends for which the same was founded; that we will be present at the meetings of the Society, as often as conveniently we can, especially at the anniversary Elections, and upon Extraordinary occasions: and that we will observe the Statutes and Orders of the said Society. Provided that whensoever any one of us, shall signify to the President, under his hand, that he desireth to withdraw from the Society, he shall be free from this Obligation for the future.

Dorchester   BROUNCKER PRS   Northampton

W. Devonshire   Moray   Seth Exon: James Annesley   BERKELEY

Charles Howard   Kenelme Digby   Victor Beaufort   Robert de Bresar

Cavendish   Will: Erskine   Ro: Boyle   M. Wren

Peter Wyche   G. Talbot   yester

James Shaen   Tho: Henshaw   John Wallis   Abage

Will. Holder   Goddart   John Wilkins   John Aubrey

Ant Morgan   Dudly Palmer   Geo: Ent   John Clayton

John Hoskins   Hill   Walter Pope   Henry Power

W. Cogene   Henry Oldenburg Sec.   John Pell   Ralph Bathurst

Walter Balle   Will: Balle RS   Theodore Haak   Jasper Needham

Charleton   John Evelyn   fran: Glisson   Daniel Whistler

Monkongs   Tho: Coxe   Philip Packer

Ievan Coventry   Christop. Merrett

Muggins   Abyngedon   Chr: Wren   Francis Potter

Tom: Wylde   Paul Neile   Daniel Colwall

Quatremains   William Brereton 1663   William Neile   Walkadye

Hayes   Edward Bysshe   William Brinde   Thomas Co

William Alsavis

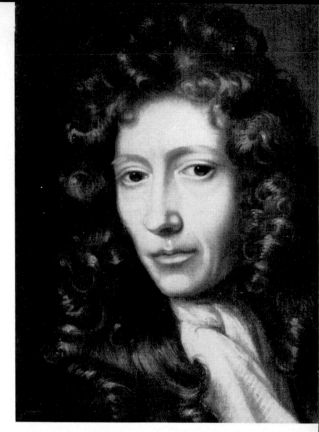

Henry Oldenburg, secretary 1671–1677 (by John van Cleef)

Robert Boyle (by J. Keerseboom)

SOME OF THE ORIGINAL FELLOWS
(from paintings in possession of the Society)

John Evelyn, secretary 1673–1675 (by Sir Godfrey Kneller)

John Wilkins, Bishop of Chester, secretary 1662–1668
(by Mary Beale)

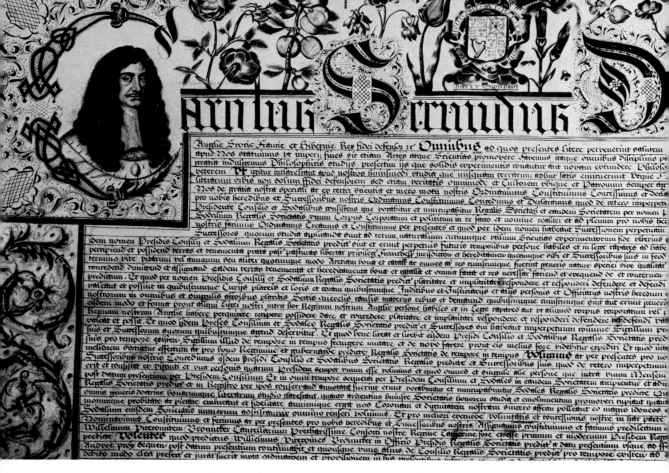

A section of the Society's second Charter, drawn up in 1663, showing a pen-and-ink drawing of Charles II.

or impossibility of a vacuum, the Torricellian experiment, the motion of falling bodies and acceleration. Theology and politics were barred. The Civil War had, however, broken out in 1642. After the victory of the Parliamentary forces in 1646, their supporters were given posts in Oxford to replace dismissed Royalists; and thus Wilkins left London in 1648 to be Warden of Wadham College, Wallis in 1649 for the Savilian chair of geometry and Goddard in 1651 as Warden of Merton College.

The meetings at Gresham College continued, and those who had migrated to Oxford attended when they happened to be in London. In Oxford they formed a similar society, meeting first in the lodgings of William Petty and, after he had left for Ireland in 1652, in Wilkins's rooms in Wadham. They were joined by Robert Boyle when he settled in Oxford in 1654; and, when Wilkins left Oxford in 1659 to become Master of Trinity College, Cambridge, they met in Boyle's lodgings. The company that thus gathered round Wilkins in Oxford proved to be very active, and this period marked a very important phase of the Society's prehistory. New members were Seth Ward, Thomas Willis, Christopher Wren, Laurence Rooke, Robert Hooke, as well as William Petty and Robert Boyle.

In the last years of the Protectorate activities in Gresham College increased, and with the Restoration the Society soon began its formal life. Of the 12 founders who made the historic decision of November 28, 1660, 10 were Royalists, one, Wilkins, was a moderate respected by the Royalists, and another, Goddard, had served Cromwell. Four of the 12—Wren, Rooke, Petty and Goddard—were at that time professors in Gresham College. Thus the Royalists and the Gresham professors were there on this occasion in force. Sir Robert Moray, soldier, courtier and friend of Charles II, informed the King of these proceedings and brought back word of the King's approval and encouragement. Moray, described by Burnet as " the life and soul " of the Society, played a great part at this time, and there is little doubt that his friendship with the King helped to ensure the granting of a Royal Charter.

A further decision was taken at this meeting to draw up a list of those " judged willing & fit to joyne with them in their designe ". The list embodied 41 names: 31 were Royalists, two had supported the Parliament, one did not join, and there are seven whose political affiliations it has not been possible to ascertain. In Restoration London it is probable that they were supporters of the King; but, even without them, the Royalist complexion of the company can scarcely be doubted. A fortnight later they resolved to admit no one to membership without scrutiny except those of the " degree of Baron or above ", while all others must be elected only when at least 21 members were present and not on the day of nomination. These rules ensured that the Royalist predominance would be maintained. The Society being now formally constituted, the King acceded to a petition for a royal grant of incorporation and discussed with Moray and John Evelyn a suitable title. On July 15, 1662, the First Charter passed the Great Seal and the Society became The Royal Society of London for " further promoting by the authority of experiments the sciences of natural things and of useful arts ", a title modified soon afterwards in the Second Charter of April 22, 1663, to the now familiar one—The Royal Society of London for Improving Natural Knowledge.

PRESIDENTS AND INNOVATORS

By E. N. da C. Andrade, F.R.S.

Emeritus Professor of Physics, University of London

THE first president of the Royal Society was Lord Brouncker, a mathematician of repute, but not one who can claim to have made outstanding advances in his subject. Among the 10 who followed him were Sir Christopher Wren, Samuel Pepys and Charles Montagu (afterwards Earl of Halifax), great men in very different fields, but not great figures in the history of science, although Wren carried out in his young days distinguished scientific work.

In 1703, however, Isaac Newton assumed the presidency and continued in that office until his death in 1727. He took the duties of the post very seriously, presiding at nearly every meeting—and in those days meetings took place every week, except during vacation time. Until Newton became president the meeting day had been Wednesday, but this was the day for certain special duties at the Mint, of which Newton had been Master since 1699. The day was therefore changed to Thursday and has remained so ever since,

a little known record of Newton's presidency.

Newton is the greatest figure in the history of the exact sciences, and has been acclaimed as such by men of science from contemporaries such as Leibniz and de l'Hôpital—who asked whether Newton ate, drank or slept like ordinary men (" for I picture him to myself as a celestial genius ")—to Eddington and Einstein in our times. This is no place to do more than name the greatest of his achievements : the deduction of the motion of heavenly bodies from three simple laws of motion and one law of universal gravitation; the foundation of mathematical physics; the establishment of the science of optics in the modern sense; the invention of the infinitesimal calculus.

Publication of the *Principia* in 1687 established his fame throughout Europe, for even where it was not understood it was accepted as the work of an exceptional genius. During his presidency the position he occupied in the world of learning

John Tyndall (1820–1893), a natural philosopher whose brilliant elucidation of the blue sky made a meteorological milestone.

Sir Frederick Gowland Hopkins, O.M., physiologist and Nobel Laureate; president of the Society, 1930–1935.

was unique: he was the object of reverence and respect such as no man of science has since inspired. When he died his body lay in state in the Jerusalem Chamber and his pall was supported by the Lord High Chancellor, two dukes and three earls. Such glory reflected credit on the Royal Society, which flourished under his leadership. Those active in his time included the famous astronomers Halley and Flamsteed, and the mathematicians Cotes, Brook Taylor, McLaurin and De Moivre, men whose like did not appear in the decades following his decease.

The seven presidents who succeeded him included some distinguished men,

but none known either for great scientific achievement or for great services to the Society. In 1778, however, Sir Joseph Banks, a most forceful character, was appointed to the Chair, and he occupied it until his death 41 years later, the longest presidency in the history of the Society. He is not known for any great scientific discovery, but he was a rich man with an amateur passion for botany, who devoted much of his time and fortune to the welfare of the Society. As a young man he saw in Captain Cook's voyage in the Endeavour, originally planned with astronomical and geographical ends alone in view, a great opportunity for gathering new knowledge

PHILOSOPHIÆ

NATURALIS

PRINCIPIA

MATHEMATICA.

Autore *JS. NEWTON*, *Trin. Coll. Cantab. Soc.* Matheseos
Professore *Lucasiano*, & Societatis Regalis Sodali.

IMPRIMATUR·
S. PEPYS, *Reg. Soc.* PRÆSES.
Julii 5. 1686.

Title page of Newton's
immortal *Principia*,
published in 1687.

LONDINI,

Jussu *Societatis Regiæ* ac Typis *Josephi Streater.* Prostat apud
plures Bibliopolas. *Anno* MDCLXXXVII.

James Watt, inventor of the steam engine, after whom a unit of electricity was named.

Sir Charles Sherrington, O.M., Nobel Laureate for pioneer work in experimental neurology.

of botanical science and natural history in general, and he arranged to accompany the great explorer. He took with him at his own expense a skilled staff admirably prepared for assembling and classifying specimens of scientific significance, and accumulated a valuable collection of the wonders of a new world. On his return to England he found himself famous.

To quote a biographer, he was " gifted with a manly presence and a genial but dignified manner ", and he became a popular figure in society and a friend of King George III, who through him took a lively interest in many activities of the Royal Society. One result of this friend-

ship was an extension and enrichment of the Royal Gardens at Kew. As president, Banks entertained men of science, British and foreign, on a lavish scale, and ruled with a benevolent if determined authority. Under him the Society regained much of the reputation it had enjoyed under Newton as a body actively promoting scientific research in all fields and became deeply respected throughout Europe.

In the year that Banks died, Sir Humphry Davy was elected president. He was a country lad who early became known as a great discoverer and a brilliant lecturer. He was the first to reveal the anaesthetic properties of nitrous oxide—" laughing

Edmond Halley, of Halley's
Comet fame.

gas "—and his work on electro-chemistry
led to the discovery of sodium and
potassium when he was 28. His discovery
of the miner's safety lamp made him
something of a national hero. He married
a rich wife and sought to become a social
figure. His new habits did not contribute
to his popularity among men of science,
but he did his best to further the interests
of the Society during his seven years as
president. He remains one of the great
scientific figures of the nineteenth century.

Three famous astronomers — William
Parsons, Earl of Rosse, who built the great
reflecting telescope that was an excitement
in Victorian times; Sir Edward Sabine,
who did much to establish the science of
terrestrial magnetism; and Sir George

Biddell Airy—occupied the chair during
the nineteenth century. With them should
be mentioned Sir William Huggins, who
carried out his fundamental work on the
composition of light from the heavenly
bodies during this century, although his
presidency ran from 1900 to 1905.

T. H. Huxley, who held the presidency
for two years only, was a national figure
as the centre of the great Darwin con-
troversy. He was particularly known for
his great gifts as a debater and essayist
and for his public services in connexion
with education. Lifelong friends of his
were the botanist Sir Joseph Dalton Hooker,
who was president before him, and John
Tyndall, who was a fellow for 41 years
but never president. Tyndall was also a

Michael Faraday, discoverer
of electromagnetic induction
in 1831.

great lecturer and a great controversialist, whose presidential address to the British Association at Belfast in 1874 evoked nation-wide dispute. He was likewise much in the public eye as a mountaineer.

Another president in the Victorian era who was a great public figure was William Thomson, Lord Kelvin, who was the first man to be raised to the peerage for his services to science. He held the chair from 1890 to 1895. He was an outstanding innovator who as a young man took a leading part in founding the science of thermodynamics. He made important contributions to the science of electricity, and he effected fundamental improvements in the mariner's compass, a service that was of great importance when steel ships were

being introduced. He was probably best known to the world for his work on submarine telegraphy which made the transatlantic cable a practical proposition. He gave a famous series of lectures in the United States. Altogether, and deservedly, he was one of the best known figures of his time. He died in 1907.

Sir George Gabriel Stokes, who preceded him as president, was world famous for his work on theoretical physics. Another great physicist was Lord Rayleigh. His *Theory of Sound*, first published in 1877, dealt with the theory of vibrations in general. It was one of the most famous books in science and is still freely consulted. Besides being a pioneer in theory, Rayleigh was a most accurate experimenter.

34

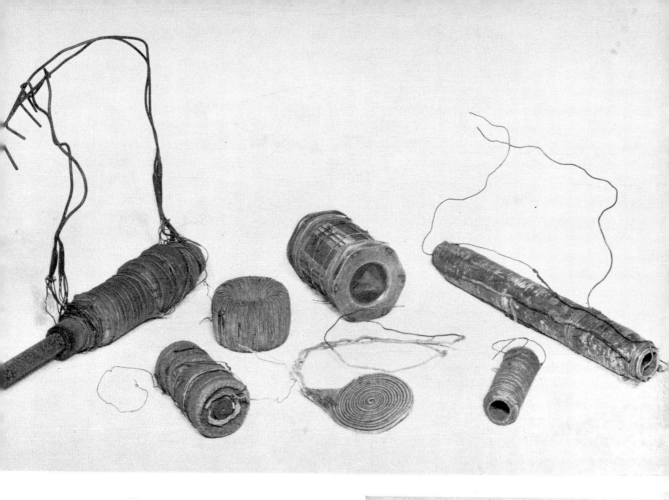

The iron ring (below) and electromagnet (right) and induction coils (above) of Michael Faraday, in the possession of the Royal Institution.

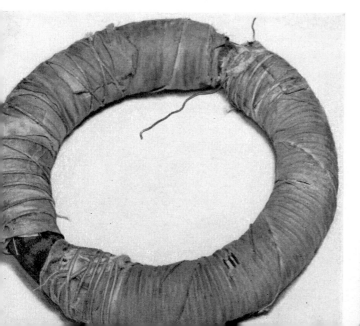

Sir Isaac Newton's reflecting telescope, which he invented in 1671.

Sir Humphry Davy's experiments in safety lamps for miners, the final version of which he invented in 1816.

After this, the great advances in physics that led to the modern view of the structure of the atom are represented by Sir William Crookes, president from 1913 to 1915; Sir Joseph John Thomson (1915-1920); and Lord Rutherford (1925-1930). Crookes, who discovered the element thallium, improved the technique of producing a high vacuum and directed particular attention to the cathode rays, which he proved to consist of negatively charged particles. With brilliant foresight he foretold the existence of isotopes, later the subject of classic researches by Aston. Thomson, making use of cathode rays, established the properties of the electron and founded a great school of research at Cambridge in which, among many other famous figures, Rutherford and Aston were trained. His speculations about the structure of the atom directed particular attention to the subject. Rutherford established the existence and nature of radioactive transformations, clearly proving that the atom was not necessarily a stable and unbreakable structure. Later he demonstrated the nuclear structure of the atom that dominates much of modern physics. He is one of the greatest figures in the history of the Society.

Rutherford was followed by Sir Frederick Gowland Hopkins, in turn succeeded by Sir William Henry Bragg, who, with his son, Sir Lawrence Bragg, established the analysis of crystal structure by means of X-rays. Sir Henry Dale rendered invaluable services as president during the very difficult war period from 1940 to 1945. After him Sir Robert Robinson, the greatest organic chemist of our time, headed the Society, followed by Lord Adrian who, like Sir Charles Sherrington, is a leader in experimental neurology.

Almost every outstanding British man of science has been a fellow of the Royal Society, so that to deal with all the great innovators would be merely to give a catalogue of names. To take the steam engine and internal combustion engine alone, one need only mention Thomas Savery, James Watt, Charles Parsons, F. W. Lanchester and Sir Frank Whittle to indicate the nature of the task. Darwin's work is so well known that it suffices to mention his name. Another great figure was Michael Faraday, the prince of experimenters, whose fundamental discoveries in electricity and magnetism are at the basis not only of much of modern physics but also of electrical engineering. The centenary of his discovery of electromagnetic induction was marked by a great celebration in 1931, attended by international figures.

Another big name is that of James Clerk Maxwell, perhaps the leading theoretical physicist of the nineteenth century who, giving Faraday's laws mathematical form, founded the electromagnetic theory of light, which stimulated Heinrich Hertz to the discovery of wireless waves. In this way most of the great scientific discoveries of the past 300 years are linked with the Royal Society, particularly if it be remembered that foreign men of genius, like Louis Pasteur, were elected to and encouraged by the Society. The men who have been mentioned in this brief account are certainly among those who best typify the work and fame of the Royal Society, but an impressive collection could still be compiled from those not mentioned here.

PATIENT WORK—then the flash of genius

By Sir Harold Hartley, G.C.V.O., F.R.S.

BY its first Charter in 1662 the Royal Society was constituted as a completely independent body to be governed by its officers and a council of 21 fellows, as it remains today. Unlike the French Academy, it had no government subsidy, and this independence the Society has always carefully maintained. In its early days amateurs like Samuel Pepys, who knew no science but became presidents, were equally welcome as fellows with the scientists to give the newly fledged Society the benefit of their moral and financial support.

It was nearly two centuries before the fellowship of the Society was restricted to scientists by the Statutes of 1847, which laid down strict rules for the choice of candidates and limited their number. As the president has said, " The choice of its fellows is in many ways the most important of the activities of the Society, just as nature herself places the perpetuation of the species as a first charge on most of her business ".

Each fellow on signing the roll must take the obligation of allegiance that has remained unchanged since 1663: " We . . . do hereby promise each for himself, that we will endeavour to promote the good of the Royal Society of London for improving Natural Knowledge, and to pursue the ends for which the same was founded."

The records of the discoveries and inventions associated with their names show the assiduity with which the fellows have fulfilled that obligation. The achievements of the fellowship have been the individual contributions of the fellows, often associated in some common task, and it cannot be claimed that the Society has contributed directly, except in so far as it has provided the opportunities for friendly gatherings and discussions, to the means of publication and, in recent years, financial support of many individuals and their work. The Society embraces all the sciences, both pure and applied, and thus it acts as a central nervous system for science both in Britain and the Commonwealth. Many of the fellows are heads of important schools of research, and Jean Ingelow's lines will strike a chord of memory in many minds:

> You were to me the world's interpreter,
> The man that taught me Nature's
> unknown tongue.

The personal influence of the fellows has made itself felt in many ways, even in the pre-natal years of the Society. It was the reputation of John Wilkins, the Jules Verne of his generation, that drew Lawrence Rooke and Christopher Wren to Wadham in the early 1650s, and his invitation brought Robert Boyle to Oxford in 1654 to join the circle that Seth Ward called "the Clubb". This provided incentive and encouragement for these young men, and supplied Gresham College in London with five of its early professors. It was at Willis's suggestion that Boyle engaged Robert Hooke as his assistant. Hooke's mechanical skill produced the air pump which played an important part in his investigation of the vacuum This was followed by his famous experiments that led to Boyle's Law, in which Hooke certainly had a hand. In 1662 Boyle released Hooke to become the Curator of the Royal Society with the duty of furnishing the Society "every day they mett, with three or four considerable experiments". Hooke quickly became the mainspring of the Society's meetings and remained so for 40 years. Wren, the many-sided genius of that early group, finding that his brilliant scientific ventures in many fields were overtopped by others, abandoned science for architecture and became the most famous architect in Europe.

Gradually the Royal Society with its *Philosophical Transactions* became the accepted medium for the discussion and publication of scientific work. Even the shy and reticent young Newton in 1671 sent his reflecting telescope, made with his own hands, to the Society for its consideration, and he submitted his classic papers on the nature of light and colour. Later, in 1685, Halley persuaded Newton to give his *Principia* to the world and bore the financial risk of its publication as the Society was in financial straits.

The mid-eighteenth century was a lean time for British science, but towards its end, under the Presidency of Sir Joseph Banks, its brilliance was revived by Cavendish, Priestley and others. Banks himself exercised great influence both at home and abroad. It was Banks's influence in Paris and London that secured safe conduct for both British and French explorers in the years when the two countries were at war, and preserved unbroken the contacts between the scientists of the two nations.

There is no better example of the interplay of one mind on another than the results of the visits of Priestley and Blagden to Paris at critical moments in the develop-

First royal page in the Charter Book, with Charles II's signature. Below: signatures of Rutherford and Flamsteed (the first Astronomer Royal).

ment of Lavoisier's revolutionary reform of chemistry. From Priestley, Lavoisier learnt of the experiments that led him to the recognition of oxygen, and from Blagden of Cavendish's discovery of the composition of water. His last remaining difficulties were thus solved, and his rational theory of combustion opened a new chapter not only for chemistry but also for the physiology of man, animals and plants, as it explained the nature of the metabolism which is the basis of life.

Lavoisier died under the guillotine in 1793, at the height of his powers. His unfinished work was continued by others, largely by Humphry Davy and by the famous Swede, Berzelius (F.R.S. 1813). Davy, by his isolation of potassium from potash, confirmed Lavoisier's view of its composition, and he also showed that Lavoisier had carried analogy too far in assuming the presence of oxygen in all acids. Berzelius was engaged in a herculean effort to make a quantitative survey of all

41

Berzelius, whose *Larbok* laid the foundation of modern chemistry.

substances, when in 1808 Dalton's Atomic Theory gave him in a flash the clue that he lacked, and with its help he made atomic composition the basis of his great *Larbok*, the forerunner of all systematic text books of chemistry. It was the generous Berzelius who wrote the epitaph of Davy, his old rival: "*le plus grand chimiste de son siècle*".

It is characteristic of the eager curiosity of man about the secrets of nature that while most of the active fellows have been professionals, the fellowship has also included men of independent means like Robert Boyle, Charles Darwin, William Parsons (the Earl of Rosse) and Lord Rayleigh, whose contributions were made in their own laboratories or observations.

Others with more slender resources devoted their leisure hours to science. Stephen Hales, the minister of Teddington, was the father of plant physiology. William Herschel, a musician and composer, in 1772 became interested in astronomy and determined to make a " review of the sky " in order to discover the distribution of the stars in space. In 1781, with a telescope made (like Newton's) with his own hands, he discovered the planet Uranus and King George III made him " the King's Astronomer ". Herschel always called his planet *Georguim Sidus* in honour of the King. Joseph Priestley was a

Lavoisier, the revolutionizer of chemistry, and his wife, in 1778. He was guillotined in 1793.

Unitarian minister with a genius for experiment.

Faraday, a bookbinder's apprentice, was dreaming of the unity of nature's forces and experimenting in his spare time until in 1813, by a stroke of fortune, Davy took him to the Royal Institution. There he helped Davy in that fortnight of brilliant investigation in 1815 that established the principle of the safety lamp for miners and saved many lives. Faraday soon began to carry out investigations himself, and from 1816 his published papers show his ability as a practical chemist who had a wide range of interests but avoided theory.

Meanwhile he continued to experiment on the relation between electricity and magnetism, until in 1831 his dream came true with his discovery of the induction of an electric current by a moving magnet, the basis of all electrical machinery. That was the turning point of Faraday's career. There is no greater contrast in scientific literature than his earlier chemical papers, with their essentially practical outlook and the brilliant flights of imagination that inspired his *Experimental Researches in Electricity*. As Kohlrausch said of him, " he smells the truth ". One discovery after another revealed more intimately the relations between electricity and magnetism, and finally the discovery of the magnetic rotation of the plane of vibration of light showed the connexion between them.

Faraday was not a mathematician, but it was his visual picture of the relations between electricity, magnetism and light that inspired the efforts of Lord Kelvin (then William Thompson) and later of Clerk Maxwell to give his ideas mathematical form and precision, culminating in the latter's electromagnetic theory of light, with the conclusive experimental evidence of its validity. The next step from Clerk Maxwell's theory was Hertz's investigation of resonating circuits, the basis of wireless, radar and radio-astronomy. All can be traced back to Faraday's intuitive perception of nature's ways.

The publication of *The Origin of Species* in 1859 was probably the greatest intellectual landmark of the nineteenth century, as it put in a clear form the theory of evolution that had long been floating in men's minds, and profoundly affected thought not only in science but in religion, philosophy and politics. The turning point in Darwin's life was his voyage in the Beagle in 1831 to 1836, which he owed to Peacock (F.R.S. 1818). In the long years of the incubation of his theory at Downe House in Kent he was influenced much by Sir Charles Lyell and Joseph Hooker, but the flash of inspiration had come from his chance reading of the *Essay on Population* by Malthus (F.R.S. 1818) in 1838. Darwin postponed publication until all his evidence was marshalled, but in 1858 Wallace sent him the draft of a paper with an identical point of view. He also had been inspired by the recollection

PHILOSOPHICAL
TRANSACTIONS:
GIVING SOME
ACCOMPT
OF THE PRESENT
Undertakings, Studies, and Labours
OF THE
INGENIOUS
IN MANY
CONSIDERABLE PARTS
OF THE
WORLD.

Vol I.

For *Anno* 1665, and 1666.

In the *SAVOY*,
Printed by *T. N.* for *John Martyn* at the Bell, a little without *Temple-Bar*, and *James Allestry* in *Duck-Lane*, Printers to the *Royal Society*.

Presented by the Author May. 30th 1667.

Title page of the first volume of the *Philosophical Transactions*, still published today.

of the Malthus essay when lying stricken by fever in Singapore. The happy sequel to this remarkable coincidence was the publication of their two essays on the theory of natural selection, followed by *The Origin of Species* a year later.

The Great Exhibition of 1851, the conception of the Prince Consort (F.R.S. 1840) was another landmark and of its fruits none has done more for science than the scholarships that have brought many young scientists to Britain. When Rutherford gained an 1851 Exhibition Research Scholarship in New Zealand in 1894 it was the fame of J. J. Thomson that drew him to Cambridge, just as the name of Wilkins had brought young men to Oxford in earlier years. Rutherford, Townsend and

McLennan were the first recruits to the great school of research in the Cavendish Laboratory, where "J. J." was soon to demonstrate the existence of the electron and discover its properties, and C. T. R. Wilson was developing the cloud chamber technique, without which the new subatomic particles might have gone undiscovered.

Rutherford left Cambridge in 1898 to go to McGill and returned 20 years later to succeed "J. J." and continue the great tradition of the Cavendish Laboratory. He had made three great discoveries that changed profoundly our views of the nature of matter. At McGill he showed that the behaviour of radioactive atoms was due to their spontaneous disintegration.

Priestley's electrical machine is at the Royal Society.

At Manchester he discovered the nature of the atomic nucleus, one of the most far-reaching discoveries of all time, and he accomplished the first artificial transmutation of one element to another by bombarding nitrogen with alpha particles.

These are some of the great episodes of scientific progress associated with the fellowship, in which the interplay of one mind on another has played so essential a part. In spite of their dramatic character, the progress of science has not been discontinuous and dependent entirely on these great advances. Sudden and unexpected as these episodes may seem, they were the outcome of the patient work of bygone generations, until some new interpretation came with a flash of genius.

HOW WORK IS FINANCED

By Sir William Penney, K.B.E., F.R.S.

Treasurer of the Royal Society

WHEN the Royal Society was founded there were no endowments, and the Society depended on its fellows for financial support. Charles II took a personal interest in the Society, in large measure due to the influence of Sir Robert Moray, but he was unable to assist with the financial support that the Society needed. The cash at the Exchequer at the time of Charles's return was only £11 2s. 10d. An annual sum of £1,200,000 was guaranteed to the King by Parliament, but in no year did he receive as much; in the first year of his reign only £70,000 was provided for ordinary expenditure. The Society quickly recognized that it would have to depend on such resources as it could command, and the council discussed at length and on many occasions various means whereby the finances might be increased. The Society's work must have involved considerable expenses, which had to be defrayed by the fellows themselves. The need for additional funds was so urgent that, in the year in which the first charter was granted (1662), application was made to the King for a grant of lands or other property in Ireland, where the Duke of Ormond, the Lord-Lieutenant, was charged with the rearrangements of confiscated property. The King even wrote personal letters to the duke strongly recommending the Society for a liberal contribution. As nothing came of the royal appeal the Society in 1663 directly petitioned the duke himself, but without success. In 1669 the King granted Chelsea College and its lands to the Society; nevertheless, some 12 years later he recovered possession for the sum of £1,300, in order to build a hospital for sick and wounded soldiers.

William Ball was the first treasurer; his duties cannot have been heavy, but the neglect of many fellows to pay the fees and subscriptions due from them to the Society caused him anxiety and often made it difficult for him to meet obligations, or even to pay the salaries of its staff. On his retirement in 1663 he presented the Society

49

with an iron-bound wooden treasure chest, in which cash and documents of value could be kept, and this box is still in the Society's possession.

The subscription payable by fellows was fixed at 1s. a week, and it was not until 1847 that it was increased to £4 a year. Some of the early fellows were extremely remiss in paying the subscription. At the end of 1663 the membership was 131, and £158 was owed—this deficit was increased by the end of 1673 to £1,957. Energetic measures had to be taken to remedy this position. Some idea of the modest beginnings of the Society may be gained by noting the expenditure for 1701: £40 was paid in salary to the clerk, £10 to the curator, £4 to the porter, and £20 10s. 7d. for heating, lighting, postage and other expenses—a total of £74 10s. 7d. for the year.

In 1709 Sir Godfrey Copley left £100 for improving natural knowledge, to be laid out in experiments or otherwise. In 1736 it was proposed that the income be used to provide a medal to be bestowed on the person whose experiment was most outstanding. This medal is the highest distinction the Royal Society can bestow. To provide a yearly bonus of £50, Sir Joseph Copley in 1881 transferred to the Society £1,666 13s. 4d. 3 per cent. Consols, such bonus to be given to the recipients of the medal. A total prize or £1,100 is now given with the medal.

On his death in 1684, Dr. William

Croone left a scheme for two lectureships he wished to found, one of which was for the Royal Society. In his will, however, he made no provision for carrying out this purpose, but his widow bequeathed to the Society one-fifth of the rent of the King's Head Tavern, Lambeth Hill, for the support of a lecture. In 1915 the property was sold, and the Society now receives from the Charity Commissioners one-fifth of the income, which is paid to the lecturer.

The first gift by a fellow (Dr. W. H. Woolaston) to the Society specifically for advancing scientific research was made in 1828; this gift was £2,000 in trust, to which other fellows added, and the fund began with a capital of £3,410. Later donors and testators have generously followed this example.

Mr. J. W. Lubbock, a bank director, was elected treasurer in 1830, and during his tenure the accounts were put on a more businesslike foundation. In 1831 appeared in print the first detailed statement of the Society's financial position for the year to November 30, 1831—previously fellows were merely told at each anniversary meeting the total receipts and payments and the balance held by the treasurer at that date. This statement showed an opening balance of £122 0s. 2½d., income £4,081 16s. 5d., payments £3,428 8s. 10d., leaving a credit balance of £775 7s. 9½d.; the capital totalled £22,582.

The Society prevailed on the Government in 1748 to spend £1,000 in providing new instruments for the Royal Observatory at Greenwich; in 1762 and 1769 it also requested and received a total of £5,600 to meet the expenses of observing the transit of Venus in those two years. The Society did, however, support scientific work from its own funds when finances permitted, and in 1774 is recorded a grant of £600 to Dr. N. Maskelyne, the then Astronomer Royal. In 1850 the first grant was made by the Government of £1,000 a year for five years to the Society, with the request to administer it for the " promotion of scientific enquiries ". The grant was demonstrably used to great advantage, and the Government placed this sum in the estimates for 1856-57 for parliamentary sanction. Since then the contributions from public funds have appeared annually in the estimates as a grant-in-aid for scientific investigations, and some idea of the growth of this aspect of the Society's work may be gained by the following figures: 1876, £5,000; 1920, £6,000; 1936, £7,000; 1946, £21,000; 1960, £75,000.

By 1934 the accounts were becoming larger and more complicated and comparison with previous years is no longer easy to make. The funds were now grouped under four headings: those referring to the general purposes of the Society over which it has full control; the special funds available only for the purposes specified by the donors and testators cover-ing library, pensions, medals, lectures, &c.; the research funds devoted to improving natural knowledge; and parliamentary grants given not for the Society's own purposes but for specified scientific objects. The table appended indicates the growth of funds and shows clearly the growing importance of scientific research in the activities of the Society; it will be seen that over the past 30 years the income devoted to research now exceeds those of the general purposes and the special funds combined.

The Society is fortunate in having the freely given services of the members of its Investment Advisory Committee who, since 1952, have advised the treasurer on the most advantageous way of investing funds not restricted to trustee securities, and the Society has greatly benefited from such advice.

During the latter part of the nineteenth century, several bequests or gifts were made to the Society for the purpose of founding medals to be awarded for eminent work in some specified field of scientific research; they included the two Royal Medals, founded by George IV in 1825, awarded annually now for the two most important contributions to the advancement of natural knowledge, one each in the biological and physical divisions of science; the Davy Medal, which was founded in 1869, to be given annually for work in chemistry; the Darwin Medal, founded in 1888, to be awarded biennially

51

A section of the library of the Royal Society. Publications on scientific matters are received from countries in all parts of the world.

for biological research; the Buchanan Medal, established in 1894, to be given quinquennially for work in hygienic science; the Sylvester Medal, in 1897, to be given triennially for the encouragement of mathematical research. In 1900 Professor Hughes left a sum of £4,000 to provide the Hughes Medal and gift, which was to be awarded annually for original discovery in physical science. Every year the council had to award several of these medals, and in 1900 they came to the decision, after many years' experience, that it was neither to the advantage of the Society nor in the interests of the advancement of natural knowledge that this long list of medals should be further increased. They decided, therefore, that no further bequests to be awarded as prizes for past achievements should be accepted.

The gradual but steady increase in the Society's own resources enabled the council to increase the financial support for scientific research. One example can perhaps be quoted: for about six years—from 1924 onwards—the greater part of the income of the Mond Fund had been accumulated and invested, by which time a sum of nearly £15,000 had been saved. This sum the council contributed in 1931 towards the construction and equipment of the Royal Society Mond Laboratory at Cambridge, which was opened in 1933. In present times the Society supports research in various ways. First, by financing research appointments, which for the current year total 22; work is being done among other subjects on various problems in physiology, cosmic ray physics, the chemistry of solids and the study of atmospheric winds by radio method. Secondly, by organizing Commonwealth bursaries, financed by the Nuffield Foundation, certain Commonwealth countries and a grant-in-aid, whereby approximately 20 bursars are assisted annually in extending their studies by visiting other countries for limited periods. Thirdly, by financing and supervision of expeditions and by supporting international research institu-

tions such as the Naples Zoological Station. Fourthly, by sending delegates to international congresses and making travel grants to research workers to visit overseas institutions and congresses. Fifthly, by building up an international scientific information service through the collection of publications and reports. Sixthly, by its publications, which now constitute a major part of the Society's efforts. The gross income from sales of publications for the year 1959 was £57,573—a far cry from the £47 received during the period 1701 to 1722 for the sale of the first publication of the Society.

The Society has sponsored many expeditions for scientific purposes. The earliest was Halley's expedition of 1676 to St. Helena to make a map of the southern stars, and they include the voyages of Captain Cook. Recently, the Society was responsible for the preparation of the United Kingdom contribution to the International Geophysical Year, and was responsible for administering a Government grant of some £600,000. Until recently the Society also made the necessary disbursements to universities engaged on space research work.

An appeal was launched, in this the tercentary year, for funds to meet increasing needs. The support given by individuals, by various bodies, and by British industry has been warm and generous. Thus, the finances of the Society are still growing as the size and influence of the Society

TERCENTENARY WINDOW.
—Commissioned by the Society, designed by Mr. William Gardner, executed by Whitefriars Glass Works, London, and installed at the Society's headquarters earlier this month.

grows. There seems to be no limit to the progress that can be made in widening the bounds of natural knowledge.

The Society is part of the British heritage in science, and by the work of its fellows and the means so generously provided by its benefactors will strive to maintain the proud position it has always enjoyed.

Year	Number of Funds		Value of Securities			Grants-in-Aid
	Special	Research	General Purposes	Special Funds	Research Funds	
			£	£	£	£
1875 ..	6	2	50,000	11,014	15,816	
1900 ..	12	8	81,076	46,200	40,200	
1913 ..	13	19	71,069	43,700	57,330	
1929 ..	18	24	87,528	55,800	506,200	
1938 ..	21	27	129,217	124,493	603,421	15,500
1959 ..	35	39	317,292	225,215	1,692,807	183,000

CLOSE TIES WITH THE COMMONWEALTH

By Lord Adrian, O.M., F.R.S.

Master of Trinity College, Cambridge

Although it regards its connexion with London with justifiable pride, the Royal Society has from the first maintained with scientists overseas strong links that have transcended both politics and war through the centuries.

WHEN the Royal Society was founded 300 years ago a great deal of the world was still unexplored and a great deal of scientific effort was directed towards the improvement of navigation. The main problem was to find a reliable method for determining the longitude of a ship at sea; without it voyages of exploration across great oceans were bound to be a hazardous business. Indeed navigation was so handicapped that Christopher Wren, elected Professor of Astronomy at Gresham College in 1657, could say in his inaugural lecture that there was hardly anything more glorious to be aimed at in art than the knowledge of longitude.

The improvement in the theory and practical construction of clocks held out

the surest hope of a solution, but it was not until the middle of the eighteenth century that the first reliable chronometers were made by Harrison. For this he was awarded the Copley Medal by the Society in 1749, but it is worth recording that Robert Hooke, the first curator, came within measurable distance of it in 1660. He was the greatest inventive genius of the age, and he had made a number of practical devices for the improvement of "artificial timekeepers" for use at sea, many of which were afterwards used in the early chronometers. But his work at the Royal Society, his poverty and his uneasy temperament kept him from following up this particular line of research. If he had done so, it must have been at the expense of his many remarkable achieve-

Captain James Cook, 1729-1779, whose experiments on diet during his Pacific voyages led to the discovery of a cure for scurvy.

ments in other lines, but the history of the world might have gone differently if the ship's chronometer had been perfected in the time of Charles II.

In the earliest numbers of the *Philosophical Transactions* of the Royal Society there are many letters from correspondents in distant countries recording natural curiosities, plants, minerals, methods of cultivation, and so forth. The earliest resident in the colonies to be a fellow was John Winthrop, Governor of Connecticut, who carried a loyal address to Charles II in 1662 and was elected in that year. The next was William Penn, who presented his map of Pennsylvania to the Society and was elected in 1681. Thereafter the list of fellows from the American Colonies contains many well-known names—Cotton Mather, Boyston and Brattle from Boston, Elihu Yale and, of course, Benjamin Franklin. The name of that amazing man does indeed stand out in the lists of the not particularly distinguished fellows elected in the middle of the eighteenth century. But apart from its North American connexions the Society elected fellows from Jamaica (Thomas Hoy in 1707 and Henry Barham in 1717) and others from the West Indies after them.

In the second half of the eighteenth century the American connexion changed

Douglas Mawson, one of the pioneers of the Antarctic.

Professor Sir Frederick Banting, of the University of Toron who discovered insulin.

its character with the war of Independence, and by then the science of navigation was revealing new parts of the world. This led ultimately to the great enlargement of the territories linked with Britain, and the Royal Society can claim to have played its part in the preliminary stages. It did so by organizing an expedition to observe the transit of Venus in 1769 and arranging that Mr. Joseph Banks with a staff of seven assistants should go in the ship Endeavour, commanded by Lieutenant James Cook.

Banks (afterwards Sir Joseph) was a wealthy landowner, a fellow of the Society with a taste for natural history and for exploring. He had already been on an expedition to Newfoundland and Labrador to collect specimens, and the voyage in the Endeavour was planned to study the Pacific regions as well as to observe the transit of Venus from Otaheite. Lieutenant (later Captain) Cook was a superb commander for such an expedition. From Tahiti they shaped a course for New Zealand. The inhabitants were hostile, but Banks collected specimens and Cook circumnavigated the islands and found that they were separated by a strait and were not part of a larger territory.

58

hn Winthrop, Jr., 1606-1676, Governor of Connecticut and whaven, was elected a fellow in 1663. He was the first resident in the colonies to be a fellow.

Benjamin Franklin, the American philosopher, scientist and statesman; one of the most influential and versatile of the early fellows.

They decided not to search for a southern continent near the Antarctic circle, but to go west to the coast of New Holland and then north to look for the lands seen by Quiros in 1606. On April 28, 1770, they entered Botany Bay and landed in what was to be New South Wales.

On the voyage north the Endeavour came near to disaster on the shoals inside the Great Barrier Reef, and the stay for repairs in Batavia brought down most of the crew with fever; but the Endeavour anchored again in the Downs in July, 1771, after an absence of three years. The voyage was soon famous, and the travellers were

summoned to Windsor for an interview with George III. Cook was made a fellow of the Society in 1776. Banks never visited the Southern Hemisphere again, as he was elected president of the Royal Society in 1778 and continued in office until his death in 1820. But his interest in New Zealand and Australia never flagged. He gave expert advice to the expedition to found the penal settlement in Botany Bay in 1788, and was in constant correspondence with the governors about their difficulties with the infant colony. He was a lifelong friend of George III and had other powerful connexions. During

59

At Burlington House in 1950 the president, Sir Robert Robinson, welcomes a new Australian fellow, Mr. H. R. Marston.

the Napoleonic Wars the Government had little time to spend on Australian affairs, and it is difficult to overestimate the influence Banks wielded from his presidential chair to make the colony a success.

During the nineteenth century the connexions of the Society with the countries of the Commonwealth were personal rather than official, but as universities grew up the opportunities for scientific research increased, and in the twentieth century the picture has changed rapidly. Residents in the Commonwealth have always been eligible for election, and many have been elected, but there are now vigorous scientific societies overseas linked with the Royal Society by friendship and community of interest. The role of scientists in wartime strengthened these links, and the need for more official co-operation was recognized at a conference held in London in 1941. This led in 1946 to an important gathering of

scientists from every part of the Commonwealth: the Empire Scientific Conference held by the Royal Society with the support of the Government and opened by King George VI. The conference took place in London, Oxford and Cambridge, and discussed a wide range of scientific topics of common interest in agriculture, nutrition, medicine and mineral resources, as well as practical measures to encourage the exchange of scientists and students within the Commonwealth.

The two volumes recording the proceedings of the conference illustrate the role that the parent Royal Society and the lively family of National Academies and Royal Societies overseas must play in the modern world. The advance of scientific knowledge has always been an international affair depending on a free and rapid exchange of information between scientists of every country. As long ago as 1723 the Society appointed a foreign secretary to promote this exchange, and it has always welcomed foreign scientists to its meetings. Nowadays every branch of science has its international congresses, its smaller meetings of specialists, and its journals, often with abstracts in several languages; and in all the laboratories where fruitful research goes on one can expect to find young scientists from other countries learning a new technique to take back to their universities.

It would certainly be a mistake for the Commonwealth to develop any exclusive organization to maintain its scientific status. But it would be an equal mistake to neglect the advantages gained by belonging to a group of countries organized on a common basis and having a long community of ideas and interests. University exchanges are far more easily managed when courses and degrees have a common pattern, when the young scientist from one part of the Commonwealth can make a lengthy stay in another to work for his doctorate without forfeiting his chance of academic position at home. Though there is so much cooperation on an international plane, the present scale of scientific research gives a great advantage to the large group: the workers who know one another personally, speak the same language and meet without constraint.

The chief group of scientists in the Commonwealth is still in Great Britain, but the whole force of Commonwealth scientists is already far larger and its achievements will be the greater for the opportunities it gains by a common background.

This argument applies to the basic sciences that interpret the principles of the natural world; the physics, chemistry and biology that deal with the constitution of protons or molecules or living organisms in general and have no direct concern with the problems of particular regions. Rutherford came from New Zealand and worked in Montreal and in England and would have had the same atomic transformations to study wherever he was. But there are important problems at a less fundamental level that come to light in some one part of the world and are best studied there, although their solution assists the general advances: problems of tropical medicine, malnutrition, agriculture and forestry. For these there is cooperation at the international level, but the Commonwealth is particularly well adapted for fostering research of this kind, and in all such fields it is a great encouragement to have the support of the Royal Society and of its Commonwealth associates.

The Royal Society is based in London and is proud of its connexion with the City and the capital. London will no doubt remain the most convenient centre for the organization of large scale research. But we can be proud of the great growth of science in the other countries of the Commonwealth, and we must do our best to strengthen our cooperation with them at all levels of scientific endeavour.

INTERNATIONAL BOND OF SCIENCE

By Sir Gerard Thornton, F.R.S.
Foreign Secretary of the Royal Society

THE first half of the seventeenth century saw the awakening of interest in science or "natural knowledge" in a number of European countries. Small groups of men of enquiring mind met to discuss scientific problems, to record observations and to conduct experiments. From these groups there grew up organized societies. Thus, in Italy the Accademia die Lincei was established in 1600 and survived until 1657, in which year the Accademia del Cimento was formed. During the same period in France the Cabinet Deputy and the Bureau d' Addresse de Renaudot provided meeting places for scientific men.

In England the outbreak of the Civil War made conditions difficult for such activity, but a group of men began to meet informally and hold discussions. One of them has recorded that " their first purpose was no more, then onely the satisfaction of breathing freer air, and of conversing in quiet with one another, without being ingag'd in the passions and madness of this dismal Age ". This body

of men, the forerunners of the Royal Society, was in contact with and received news of continental developments in the field of science, so that, when the Royal Society was formed in 1660 contacts with other countries already existed. Their intimacy was shown by the fact that the first list of fellows included the Frenchman Samuel Sorbière and the Dutch physicist Christiaan Huygens. John Winthrop, who was Governor of Connecticut, was also on this list. More fellows from foreign countries were added during the next 20 years.

There was considerable interest in microscopy and in microscopic anatomy among our early fellows stimulated by the invention of a compound microscope by Robert Hooke and the publication of his book *Micrographia*, in 1665, which aroused great interest abroad. Two pioneers in this field from Europe were among our early fellows: the Italian Marcello Malpighi, elected in 1668, and Antonj van Leeuwenhoek, the Dutch microscopist who first

Marie François Arrouet de Voltaire popularized
much of Newton's work abroad.

André Ampere (1775-1836), mathematician physicist,
explained electro-magnetic phenomena.

Caroleus Linnaeus, the Swedish botanist and
taxonomist, who first defined species and genera.

Antonj van Leeuwenhoek (1632-1723), Dutch microscopist,
was the discoverer of bacteria.

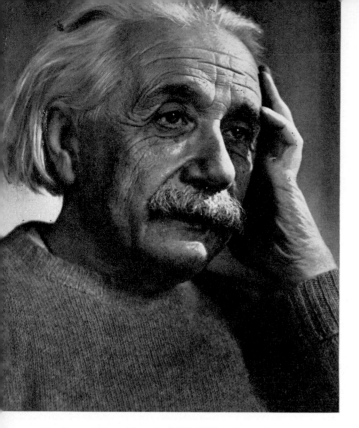

Professor Albert Einstein (1879-1955), whose theory
of relativity became a great milestone.

Dr. Louis Pasteur (1822-1895), among whose
discoveries was the cure for hydrophobia.

observed bacteria. The latter was elected in 1679 and communicated all his discoveries in the form of letters to the Royal Society that were published in the *Philosophical Transactions of the Royal Society*.

This journal was first published in 1665; its editor, Henry Oldenburg, was secretary to the Royal Society and editor for 14 years. The *Transactions* contained not only original contributions but accounts of science abroad, reviews of European works and a variety of scientific matter resulting from an extensive foreign correspondence. Sprat in his *History of the Royal Society*, published in 1667, refers to the

encouragement given to the Society by correspondence with other lands, particularly with France, Italy, Germany and the Low Countries. Indeed, he states that correspondence with Christiaan Huygens and others was maintained in spite of a state of war then prevailing between England and Holland. Henry Oldenburg got into trouble through correspondence abroad at the time when the war with Holland took a turn unfavourable to this country; in June, 1667, he was arrested and put in the Tower charged with " dangerous designs and practices ". Pepys says that he was " writing news to a

Max Planck (1859-1947), a pioneer in the field of theoretical physics and thermodynamics.

I. P. Pavlov, Russian physiologist, whose experiments with dogs led to the theory of reflexes.

virtuoso in France ". But fortunately he was released the following August.

The fame and influence of the Royal Society abroad was much enhanced by the work of Isaac Newton and especially by the publication of his *Principia*. This was particularly evident in France, where Voltaire made his work known outside scientific circles by his popular book *Elemens de la Philosophie de Newton*, published in 1738. Newton was President of the Royal Society from 1703 till he died in 1727, and during this time foreign contacts and correspondence were greatly increased. In 1719, Robert Keck, a fellow of the

Society, left £500 to be laid out by the Society, " the profits arising, to be bestowed on some one of the Fellows, whom they shall appoint to carry on a foreign correspondence ". From this legacy the office of foreign secretary had its origin.

The friendly relations maintained with scientists overseas, often transcending political differences and the state of war, is well illustrated in the person of Benjamin Franklin, whose memory we especially honour. Franklin was awarded the Copley Medal, the Society's highest award, in 1753; he was elected a fellow in 1756, and during his visits to England between 1757

65

and 1775 served on the council. During the War of Independence he was appointed American envoy in Paris. At this time James Cook was making his last voyage in the Endeavour and Franklin sent instructions to American captains and commanders of ships to spare and aid Cook on his voyage. Later when gold medals were struck in Cook's honour, Sir Joseph Banks, then President of the Royal Society, sent one to Franklin with a cordial letter. Thus were the Society's friendly relations with American science unaffected by war. They have ever since remained most cordial. Again, during the Napoleonic wars Banks did all he could to preserve friendly relations with French scientists; indeed, Cuvier and Lacépède were elected fellows in 1806 and Biot and Gay-Lussace just before Waterloo.

Organized international science began during the nineteenth century, but it was not until 1899 that an International Assocation of Academies was formed. This included the Royal Society and first met in 1900, continuing to operate until the outbreak of war in 1914. In 1918 the Royal Society took steps to revive international scientific cooperation and arranged a meeting in the Society's rooms; this was followed by a second in Paris at which preparations were made for an International Research Council. This council held its first meeting in Brussels in 1919, when Sir Arthur Schuster, the Royal Society's foreign secretary, was elected general secretary of the council. At the same time

international unions for astronomy, geophysics, geodesy, chemistry, and mathematics were formed, to be followed in 1922 by further unions for physics, scientific radio, geography, and biology. At the fifth general assembly of the council some changes were made on a proposal by the Royal Society that resulted in the council being reconstituted in 1931 under the present name of International Council for Scientic Unions (I.C.S.U.).

This council has two categories of membership, national and scientific. National members adhere to it through some academy or other organization; the Royal Society is the adhering body for the United Kingdom. The scientific members comprise the international unions. The Royal Society adheres to 12 of these unions, and for each one, has set up a national committee whose membership includes fellows as well as representatives of other relevant scientific societies and interested bodies. From 1918 till 1958 the general secretaries of the council have all been fellows of the Royal Society; its present president Sir Rudolph Peters, is also one of our fellows.

Another important activity of the I.C.S.U. is the setting up of special committees to organize specific research programmes. Of these the first and best known was that set up to organize the International Geophysical Year (I.G.Y.), by far the greatest enterprise in international cooperation in science ever planned. The very considerable British contribution to

MICROGRAPHIA:

OR SOME

Phyſiological Deſcriptions

OF

MINUTE BODIES

MADE BY

MAGNIFYING GLASSES.

WITH

OBSERVATIONS and INQUIRIES thereupon.

By *R. HOOKE,* Fellow of the ROYAL SOCIETY.

Non poſſis oculo quantum contendere Linceus,
Non tamen idcirco contemnas Lippus inungi. Horat. Ep. lib. 1.

NVLLIVS IN VERBA

LONDON, Printed by *Jo.* Martyn, and *Ja.* Alleſtry, Printers to the
ROYAL SOCIETY, and are to be ſold at their Shop at the *Bell* in
S. *Paul's* Church-yard. M DC LX V.

this scheme was formulated into a programme by the Royal Society. As part of this contribution the Society organized the I.G.Y. Antarctic Expedition and set up the Royal Society base at Halley Bay.

Two of the most important results of the I.G.Y. have been the opening up and scientific exploration of the Antarctic Continent, and the commencement of the whole new era of space research. To continue international cooperation in these fields the I.C.S.U. has set up two special committees, one on Antarctic research and one on space research. The I.G.Y. also emphasized the importance of oceanography, a special committee for which has also been established. For each of these three special committees the Royal Society has set up a national committee to coordinate the British programme.

The establishment in 1946 of Unesco resulted from discussions in which the Royal Society took part. Its first director general was Sir Julian Huxley and its first director of natural sciences was Dr. Joseph Needham, both fellows of the Society; the Minister of Education invited the Royal Society to give advice on the scientific programme of Unesco. The Society now has a committee for this purpose, assisted by panels whose members give it expert advice on each of the main aspects of that programme.

◀ **Robert Hooke's *Micrographia*, published in 1665, the first work in microscopic studies.**

68

Some measure of the Royal Society's activities in connexion with organized international science may be gauged by the fact that its council is advised on international relations by 50 committees, subcommittees and panels with a total membership of 790 persons.

Apart from this activity the Society does much to make possible the travel and exchange of scientists with other countries. Thus it has an arrangement with the Academy of Sciences of the U.S.S.R. for the annual exchange of senior lecturers and of more junior research workers. There have always been most cordial relations between the Royal Society and the British Commonwealth, all subjects of which are eligible for election to its fellowship. There is a free and considerable flow of visiting scientists between the United Kingdom and other Commonwealth countries, and the Society has sought to stimulate this by setting up in 1933 the Royal Society and Nuffield Foundation Commonwealth Bursaries Scheme whose object is to enable scientists to visit and spend some time in Commonwealth countries other than their own. It gave the Royal Society great pleasure when, in 1951, fellows resident in Australia formed the new Australian Academy of Science on a pattern similar to that of the Society and when in 1954 this academy received its Royal Charter from the hands of the Queen.

In its personal relations the Royal

Society welcomes many scientists from both Commonwealth and foreign lands at its rooms and to its scientific meetings and discussions. Its fellows take much pleasure in giving private hospitality to honoured visitors from all parts of the world. It is perhaps in this way that the Society maintains most closely the spirit of international friendship that marked its earliest years.

TO THE FOUR CORNERS OF THE EARTH

By G. E. R. Deacon, C.B.E., F.R.S.

Director, National Institute of Oceanography

IN 1698 Edmond Halley resigned his post as Clerk to the Royal Society to take charge of a scientific expedition. He had already explained the trade winds and monsoons, and now produced a chart of magnetic declination of great value to sailors. His enthusiasm and activity did very much to advance science and encourage exploration. He predicted transits of Venus across the sun's disc in two years in the eighteenth century, and although he did not live to see them, they were the subject of two scientific expeditions. The first was a Royal Society expedition to St. Helena in 1761. The Society's funds were not sufficient to meet the expense, but the President, Council and Fellows sent a Memorial to the Lords of the Treasury praying for a grant of £1,600, and it was given to them. The second transit, in 1769, was the occasion of a second Memorial and this led to Cook's voyage in the Endeavour. Mr. (later Sir

Joseph) Banks and President of the Society for 42 years, sailed in her and contributed £10,000 to the cost. He remained a generous patron of science and exploration.

The Royal Society has done much to further Arctic and Antarctic exploration. In 1773 the council wrote to Lord Sandwich, First Lord of the Admiralty, recommending an expedition to the Arctic by way of Spitzbergen. One of the minor results of the expedition under Captain Phipps in H.M.S. Racehorse was the first successful deep-sea sounding. Nelson was there as a midshipman and it was then that he fought his private battle with the Polar bear. In 1817 the Society urged renewed exploration of the North West Passage after taking note that Barrow and Scoresby had reported the disappearance of much ice from the Canadian Arctic. Ross, and afterwards Parry, were sent and they made extensive discoveries.

Science, as much as commerce, was

Reading meteorological instruments.

providing the initiative. In August, 1938, Lieutenant Colonel Sabine convinced the eighth meeting of the British Association that more should be done about terrestial magnetism. A learned committee was set up, including the Master of Trinity and the Dean of Ely. A memorial was presented to the Government, strongly supported by the Royal Society, and within a year Sir James Clark Ross and Captain Crozier were ready to sail in H.M.S. Erebus and Terror on their great voyage of discovery and research in the Southern and Antarctic regions. The editor of the *Quarterly Review* wrote, " The presentation of the Memorial was backed not only by the personal arguments and representations of its framers, but by similar and even more urgent representations on the part of the President and Council of the Royal Society, who, on this occasion, in a manner most honourable to themselves, and casting behind them every feeling but an earnest desire to render available to science the ancient and established credit of their institution, threw themselves unreservedly

and with their whole weight into the scale, with immediate and decisive effect." The achievements of the expedition were unparalleled. They explored the Ross Sea, saw the fantastic ice-barrier for the first time, made important discoveries in North Graham Land, and secured great additions to our knowledge of the ocean and of the earth's magnetism.

The same preparation and persuasion preceded the great round-the-world ocean exploration of H.M.S. Challenger in 1872-76, and the setting up of the geophysical programme of the International Geophysical Year in 1957. The task of drafting instructions for the scientific work of exploratory expeditions, which gave the Council ample opportunity to put forward plans for research of many kinds, and to support them with vigour, involved much hard work.

There were 19 meetings to select observers and to draft instructions and to provide instruments for the 1761 expedition to St. Helena. The inquiry for the voyage to the southern seas in 1839 was divided into different parts, and referred to separate committees, consisting of those members of the Society who were specially conversant with physics, meteorology, geology and mineralogy, botany and vegetable physiology, zoology and animal physiology. They produced a small volume of 100 pages, which the distinguished leader of the expedition seemed glad to receive. The same was done for H.M.S. Challenger: " the Committee of the Royal Society, with Admiral Richards as one of its most influential members, met from time to time and offered practical suggestions ". Work of the same standard has been done for many other scientific explorations and for the International Geophysical Year, and it has led to a tremendous record of scientific achievement.

The Government and the Admiralty, when convinced, have always shown themselves ready to act. The *Quarterly Review* of 1840 said: " Science is of no party. Under the government whether of Whig or Tory she has often had to complain of the difficulty of making herself heard in recommendation of her objects, but these objects once recognized by a British government are taken up in a spirit and with a liberality which ensures success." Ross remarked that " every improvement that former experience could suggest in preparing the ships for the service, and contributing to the health, comfort and safety of their crews, was granted by the Admiralty ". He would not be able to recruit all his volunteers on double pay today, but otherwise he would still get as much help from the Royal Society and the Government.

FROM FOLKLORE TO FACT

By Sir Graham Sutton, C.B.E., F.R.S.
Director-General of the Meteorological Office

THE connexion of the Royal Society with meteorology, both as a science and a profession, goes back to its earliest days. In 1663 Robert Hooke devised a scheme for daily observations of weather and in 1686 Edmond Halley published in the *Philosophical Transactions* a long essay in which he tried to identify the "phisical cause" of trade winds and monsoons. This paper also contained Halley's famous chart of the winds of the world, a first and, on the whole, surprisingly good representation of what is now called "the general circulation of the atmosphere". About 70 years later George Hadley, F.R.S., gave the correct explanation of the trade winds, and the Society's journals have always contained contributions from meteorologists.

Official meteorology began in this country in 1855, when the Board of Trade set up a Meteorological Department with Admiral Robert FitzRoy, F.R.S., in charge. This action followed an international conference in Brussels in 1853 to organize meteorological observations at sea, but before the Meteorological Department was formed the board had consulted the Royal Society "as to what are the great desiderata in meteorology". The result was a long letter, dated February 22, 1855, from the president and council laying down precisely what observations were to be made and how they were to be processed. It is interesting to note that observations of aurorae and "falling stars", and also of magnetic compass variations, were included. The document contains one or two rather naive speculations (for instance, that the primary cause of northern cyclones is "the condensation of large quantities of vapour and the consequent influx of air to supply the place"), but is most remarkable for the fact that weather forecasts are not mentioned. It seems very likely that the compilers of the letter did not regard the foretelling of weather as a genuine scientific activity.

FitzRoy had other views, and during his term of office he not only published

77

yesterday

Method employed in the early 1900s to record wind pressure, temperature and humidity.

Below: the gear shed winch and (right) a kite in flight.

today

Forecast room of the London weather centre: and a radio locator used to obtain information on the bearing and distance of lightning flashes.

storm warnings and forecasts but also drew up a long list of rules for interpreting barometer readings in terms of coming weather. When he died in 1865 the Royal Society was again consulted. A committee, under Sir Francis Galton, was strongly against the publication of forecasts. The Board of Trade solved its embarrassing problem by requesting the Society to form a committee to control the Meteorological Office. The suspension of all forecasts, including the storm warnings at ports, caused such an outcry that the Meteorological Committee was forced to restore the gale warnings, but it refused to countenance general weather forecasts. In 1877 the Meteorological Committee of the Royal Society was replaced by a paid body and in 1879 the publication of forecasts recommenced and has continued ever since, except for interruptions by war.

Today, the Royal Society exercises no direct control over the activities of the Meteorological Office, although one member of the Meteorological Committee is appointed on the advice of the president. The Society, however, still plays a considerable part in furthering meteorology as a science. It does this mainly through two bodies, the Gassiot Committee and the National Committee for Geodesy and Geophysics. The function of the Gassiot Committee (it takes its name from a bequest made by John P. Gassiot, F.R.S.,

in 1871) is to advise the Society on matters relating to research in pure meteorology and to supervise the disposal of the funds available. In recent years these funds have been mainly provided by the Air Ministry, the parent body of the Meteorological Office, and with these resources the Gassiot Committee has been able to initiate considerable meteorological research in the universities, especially into the distribution of ozone and in problems of radiation and high-atmosphere physics. This work has been invaluable in supplementing the research activities of the Meteorological Office. The Meteorology and Atmospheric Physics Sub-Committee of the National Committee for Geodesy and Geophysics is largely concerned with matters that fall outside the scope of professional meteorology in the international field.

The tradition of a strong and lively concern for the earth sciences in the Royal Society has been maintained throughout the whole of its history. The Society did much to foster the science of the atmosphere when it was emerging from folklore and today, when the status of meteorology is no longer in question, it continues to promote, help, and advise whenever an opportunity presents itself. Meteorology, not only in Britain but all over the world, owes much to the Royal Society.

CAN THE UNIVERSITIES REMAIN FREE?

By Sir Patrick Linstead, C.B.E., F.R.S.

Rector of the Imperial College of Science and Technology

LESS than 100 years ago Matthew Arnold wrote " English Universities have no science ". Today all is changed; science and the universities have come together with enormous benefit to both. Why has this happened?

Arnold's criticism, of course, at no time applied to mathematics, which from classical times had achieved a respectable place as part of a liberal education. But the experimental sciences were parvenus, children—or grandchildren—of the renaissance; their progress in the older universities of England and Scotland during the first two centuries of the age of science was essentially due to the achievement of gifted individuals. Modifications of the curriculum were negligible. " The modern world is full of artillery and we turn out our children to do battle in it equipped with the shield and sword of an ancient gladiator ", Huxley said reproachfully at the end of the epoch.

But the change had already begun with the reform of the old universities and the founding of the new; and the scientific revolution crept in like a long-delayed tide. Within a decade Oxford introduced the Honours School in Natural Science, Cambridge the Natural Science Tripos, and London the B.Sc.

Today the tide of science has come in so far (although not yet to the full) that the educational landscape of 1860 can no longer be recognized. The number of scientists and engineers who graduate annually has risen from a handful to about 10,000 and may well be double this in another decade. Some of this rise is due to a growing realization that science provides one of the most satisfying and entrancing fields of intellectual endeavour; but the main factor has surely been the voracious vocational demand. " Science " has, in fact, become a leading profession—and its professional army is officered almost

Sir Howard Florey receiving from Lord Adrian, in 1951, the royal medal for his work on antibiotic drugs, in particular penicillin.

entirely by university graduates.

Some people are asking for a change in quality as well as quantity. One suggestion is a lengthening of the first degree course to permit a deepening of the understanding of fundamentals and a broadening of interests. But it is clear that this is going to have a lower priority than the pressing need for more university places and that any immediate extension of formal education must come for selected students after graduation—perhaps some time afterwards.

The great scientific influx has undoubtedly had a vitalizing effect on the universities, but it has also created a new problem. How can the nation's need that most of the new students should be in the fields of science and technology be reconciled with the traditional freedom of the universities? The thought of any direction of labour arouses academic passions, and the situation calls for all the tact for which the University Grants Committee is so rightly famous.

The university nowadays is expected to be a centre for the advancement of natural knowledge. This was not always true. Newman, for one, believed that in a university research should be quite

82

subordinate to teaching; and we may remember that the researches of Cavendish and Priestley, Davy and Faraday were not carried out in university laboratories. Among the changes of the past 100 years has been the rise of the " research school " with Liebig in Giessen, Hofmann in London, Roscoe in Manchester, and the founding of the Cavendish and Clarendon laboratories. Ninety years ago Lockyer could complain that "true scientific research is absolutely unencouraged and unpaid ". Last year one government agency alone gave more than £2m. for the support of university research and maintained more than 2,000 research students at universities. The larger centres of university research in science and technology, such as Cambridge, the Imperial College and Birmingham, are comparable in size with the main research stations of industry or government.

University science has its peculiar glories, and its names are known to all educated men: Rutherford and Thomson, Kelvin, Huxley, Clerk Maxwell. It was in the universities that our modern conceptions of energy, matter and life emerged. They have been the home of great discoveries. They also have a unique function that is even more important; now that taxation has eclipsed the wealthy amateur, the universities are virtually the only centres in which the gifted individual can pursue natural inquiries of entirely his own choosing. They are thus the safeguard against total direction of research. The university of today is not merely a convenient home for science but the main protector of its inner spirit.

MEDICINE COMES INTO ITS OWN

By Sir Henry Dale, O.M., G.B.E., F.R.S.

WILLIAM HARVEY died in 1657, too early to be a fellow of the Royal Society. He had been physician to Francis Bacon and to Charles I; and younger physicians who must have known him and been inspired by his *De Motu Cordis* (1628)—the first and still supreme example of the advancement of medical knowledge by the then new method of experiment, which Bacon had so powerfully advocated—were prominent in the groups that began to meet about 1645, to discuss this " new " or " experimental " philosophy. They were to become the effective founders of the Royal Society, and medicine continued to be well represented among the original fellows and council. The first register (i.e., secretary) of the founding philosphers had been Dr. William Croone, whose will later founded the Royal Society's first regular lectureship, for which he prescribed a physiological subject. A generation earlier in 1600, William Gilbert, physician to Elizabeth I, had published his *De Magnete*, which marked the very beginning of experimental physics.

But it cannot be suggested that medicine, or its practitioners, continued to play a prominent part in the Royal Society's activities during the two centuries after its foundation. Physicians and, later, surgeons, continued to be elected to its fellowship, but apart from the unique emergence of a genius of Harvey's stature, it must be remembered that nearly all medicine was to remain until years within living memory a traditional empirical art. Any new knowledge added to its canon by observations at the bedside, or at autopsy, would naturally go to the royal colleges, rather than to the Royal Society, which was less concerned with such professional knowledge than with discoveries made by amateurs of genius, over the whole range of the natural sciences. Furthermore, many of the elections of medical men to the fellowship in those earlier centuries, were complimentary, like those of Church dignitaries, or of leading luminaries in the other learned professions. Even some of the elections of physicians to the Society's presidential chair were probably made to recognize public services to

A painting of King Charles I and William Harvey, his physician, which hangs in the Royal College of Physicians.

medicine and the state, rather than special scientific achievements; while others who had abandoned their medical practice—Wollaston, Thomas Young, Sir Joseph D. Hooker—were elected to presidential or other offices for outstanding research in extra-medical ranges of science: chemistry, physics, and botany.

On the other hand, chance must in that period have played an important part in determining whether discoveries, even of great importance, made in the wards or by *post-mortem* dissections would be recognized by the Royal Society, Thomas Addison, hailed now as the father of endocrinology, was never proposed for its fellowship; and there were probably other omissions almost as unfortunate.

85

Lord Lister and his assistants in the Victoria ward of King's College Hospital in 1891.

It was not until the second half of the nineteenth century that there were signs of the Royal Society becoming fully cognizant of the scientific possibilities of medicine. The appointment, in 1881, of Michael Foster, Professor of Physiology at Cambridge, to what proved to be a 20-year tenure of one of the secretaryships, marked an important step in that direction; and of still greater importance was the election as president, in 1895, of a great surgeon, Lord Lister, already world famous for the revolutionary advance he had made in surgery by his application of Pasteur's bacteriological discoveries.

Before the end of the nineteenth century the Society had also begun to co-operate with the Government in the appointment of commissions to investigate malaria (1898), African sleeping-sickness (1902), and Malta fever (1904), and in providing for the eventual publication of the results. More recently a series of major gifts and bequests have enabled the Society to appoint a succession of scientists of distinction to full-time research fellowships, and others to a number of research fellowships, in the medical sciences as well as in experimental and theoretical physics.

Between the two world wars, the Society elected as presidents two scientists of outstanding leadership in different aspects of medical research, Sir Charles Sherrington (1920-25) and Sir F. Gowland Hopkins (1930-35). They were elected in alternation with two great pioneers of modern sub-atomic physics, Sir J. J. Thomson (1915-20) and Lord Rutherford (1925-30). Sherrington's great work on the "integrative action" of the nervous system was, by general consent, to provide a new basis for the science of neurology, in the clinic as well as in the experimental laboratory; while the achievements of Hopkins, most widely known as the pioneer of research on vitamins, made him a principal founder of modern bio-chemistry, now rapidly invigorating nearly every aspect of medical research as well as functional zoology and botany.

The latest methods and instruments of electronic physics and chemistry, and leading experts in these fundamental disciplines, seem now to be finding opportunities for research in those fields that contribute more directly to the advancement of medicine—physiology, bio-chemistry, pharmacology, pathology, immunology, even genetics; and the result seems to be to strengthen and enliven research in both the sections into which the Royal Society has long been accustomed to divide its scientfic activities.

SOME RECENT ACHIEVEMENTS IN SCIENCE

I—Boom in Radio Astronomy

By Martin Ryle, F.R.S.

Professor of Radio Astronomy, University of Cambridge

AT the end of the war there were perhaps a dozen workers in the field of radio astronomy. Today the subject has grown so that in both staff and equipment, and possibly even in its potential in advancing our knowledge of the universe, it rivals optical astronomy. There are today some 65 radio astronomical observatories throughout the world, and the number is rapidly increasing.

From the early observations of the radio emission from the sun and the Milky Way there has grown a wide range of investigations; some of these represent the extension of optical methods, but in others quite unexpected phenomena have been revealed by radio telescopes.

The surface of the moon has been found to be a smooth, gently undulating plain. Radar reflections have given most of the new details of this surface, but the radio waves emitted from just below the surface can also be detected, and give a valuable measurement of temperature. Radar reflections from the planets have also been obtained, but the most important advance here is the observation of unexpectedly intense emission from some planets, which may indicate the existence of an enveloping cloud of high energy particles, like the terrestrial van Allen belt.

The exploration of the outer atmosphere of the sun and its extension into the interplanetary space has been made by observing the scattering of radio waves from a distant source as they pass near the sun.

One of the major advances made in the past few years has been in the exploration of the Milky Way system, by observing a spectral line at a wavelength of 21cm. which originates in the clouds of neutral interstellar hydrogen. It has become possible to plot out a three-dimensional distribution of the interstellar gas with a detail quite unforeseen 10 years ago; before this optical exploration was severely limited by the obscuration produced by the interstellar "dust". The observations have also revealed a remarkable situation occurring near the nucleus of the galaxy, where there appears to be a continous out-flow of matter; whatever the explanation of these observations there seems little doubt that it will be of great relevance to the theories of the evolution of the Milky Way.

Radio waves of longer wavelength have also revealed the presence of an extensive and tenuous "halo" surrounding the star system of the galaxy, which is probably related to the acceleration of cosmic ray particles in an extensive magnetic field enclosing the galaxy.

Perhaps the most exciting investigation

The 30-second eclipse of the sun on May 28, 1900, photographed at Wadesboro, N. Carolina.

In the control room of the giant radio telescope at Jodrell Bank, Cheshire.

in radio astronomy today is related to the nature of the radio stars—the intense " point " sources of radio waves that can be detected superimposed on the general emission from the Milky Way. Although the positions of about 1,000 of these sources are now known with good accuracy only some 50 have been related to optically visible objects; the rest are too faint. Some are the gaseous remains of supernovae explosions in our own galaxy and others are galaxies near by whose radio emission is comparable with that from our own.

About 12 have been related to more distant galaxies, and for some of these the radio emission exceeds that from the Milky Way by a factor of a million.

The interest of such sources lies in the fact that similar ones at, say, 10 times the distance would be unobservable by optical telescopes, yet their radio emission would still be easy to detect. The possibility or extending observations appreciably beyond the limit of the 200in. telescope greatly increases the chances of distinguishing between different cosmological models.

Two aerials of the radio interferometer being built at the Royal Radar Establishment site at Malvern.

The future of many of these investigations depends on the construction of radio telescopes of even greater size than those at present available. A 600ft. steerable paraboloid is now in course of construction in the United States at a cost of $63m., and large instruments are also being built in Russia. Fortunately new methods of " synthesizing " large radio telescopes have been developed that have already allowed major instruments to be constructed at a small fraction of the cost of such telescopes. While such instruments cannot perform some of the functions for which these large paraboloids are designed—such as the tracking of satellites and deep space probes—they may be just as valuable for purely astronomical research, and even larger instruments for these purposes may be practicable.

91

II—How Old and How Far the Stars?

By Fred Hoyle, F.R.S.

Plumian Professor of Astronomy, University of Cambridge

JUST 40 years ago Eddington proposed the basis of a solution to the puzzle of the sun's energy: that the source lies in the conversion of hydrogen to helium. The development of nuclear physics in the subsequent two decades gave much insight into the actual physical processes by which four protons can be converted into a helium nucleus under the conditions occurring in stellar interiors. This problem was thought to have been solved—refinements apart—with the work of Bethe and Critchfield in 1938; recent laboratory measurements have, however, turned up surprising results yielding a situation far more complex than nuclear physicists had expected.

A problem of immediate urgency is to determine how far the ages calculated by astrophysicists for the oldest stars in our galaxy will be affected by this new work. The present ages stand at about 20,000 million years—about four times the age of the earth. It has become apparent in the past year or two that unless this age for our galaxy can be appreciably reduced, or unless the observed distance scale of the universe is in serious error, explosive theories of the origin of the universe are disproved by the contradiction that in such theories the stars would be older than the universe itself.

Attempts are under way to redetermine the distance scale. A promising possibility lies in the optical identification of powerful distant sources of radio waves. These have been found in some cases to be galaxies containing hot gas that emits bright spectrum lines, a circumstance highly convenient for the observation of very distant objects.

Much progress has been made in the past five years towards understanding the origin of cosmic radio waves. In all really powerful sources the radio emission appears

A 74-inch reflector in revolving turret at the Radcliffe Observatory, Pretoria.

Model of the 98in. Isaac Newton reflecting telescope to be completed at Hurstmonceux in 1965 by Sir Howard Grubb Parsons & Company.

PROSPECTUS INTRA CAMERAM STELLATAM.

Two contrasting views of Greenwich Observatory.
Above: seventeenth-century astronomers at work in the Great Room at Greenwich.

Below: the Equatorial group of domes, housing six telescopes, at Hurstmonceux, Sussex.

to arise from the deflection of energetic electrons by magnetic fields. The electrons seem for the most part to be generated by the collision of cosmic ray protons with the diffuse gaseous medium that certainly lies within many galaxies and that may be present throughout space. Radio astronomy has, therefore, a dual importance in providing information both about the distribution of cosmic rays and about the structure of cosmic magnetic fields. Much active work is in progress at present on the structure of the magnetic field of our own galaxy. Moreover, the energy distribution of cosmic rays seems to be remarkably similar from one galaxy to another, and the suspicion is growing that these remarkable particles may indeed be genuinely cosmic.

Until very recently astronomers con-centrated their attention largely on galaxies that were either near (and which could accordingly be observed in great detail) or very distant, the latter in connexion with studies of the expansion of the universe. In the past year or two, however, galaxies in the middle distance have begun to receive serious attention. The outcome of the first investigations is that highly peculiar galactic states are not nearly as uncommon as was formerly supposed. Many of these states are clearly very short-lived. Several examples have been studied in which whole groups of galaxies seem to be in rapid dissolution. If confirmed, this result would require us to suppose that new galaxies are in the process of formation—a conclusion of great importance to theories of cosmology.

III—New View of Plant Life

By H. Godwin, F.R.S.

Professor-elect of Botany, University of Cambridge

DURING the past quarter of a century large changes have affected botanical science, some few dramatic and sudden, but the majority the result of sustained attack on fundamental problems with the aid of modern physico-chemical and mathematical techniques.

By the use of radioisotopes and paper chromatography we have gone a considerable distance towards understanding the nature of photosynthesis, and there is a strong probability that the oxygen produced in that process comes from the photolysis of water. The main pathways of carbohydrate metabolism are becoming known and are seen to be largely similar in plant and animal tissues. It appears that many phases of respiration occur in plants, as in animals, in discrete cellular particles, the mitochondria; and from many angles the mechanisms of cellular biology are being elucidated, notably those controlling the accumulation of ions from the external medium.

From the discoveries by Went of substances controlling plant development and metabolism, the auxins or growth substances, there has stemmed a great increase in understanding of such phenomena as the growth responses of plants and internal coordination of growth processes. From these discoveries has proceeded the vast field of research into plant hormones and phyticides, with their immensely important applications in agriculture, horticulture and forestry, to weed control, fruit set, storage and vegetative propagation. A related development is that of the antibiotics produced by micro-organisms: besides their significance to medicine, such substances play a most important role in the microcosm of the soil, most particularly in the rhizosphere that develops about the living roots.

We have indeed become far more conscious of the intricate complexity of the relationship between the living plant and its environment: the processes of vernalization and photoperiodicity have been recognized, studied and applied with great impact to practical plant husbandry. In such studies there have come into use the great phytotrons, batteries of glass houses in which the closest control of all environmental factors is attained.

To no cognate field of science does botany owe more than to genetics, the influence of which has transformed not only the crops of the world but our views on evolutionary mechanisms and the nature of wild plant populations. Partly as a result of this, plant taxonomy has itself been revitalized and its devotees now increasingly concern themselves with biometry, cytological studies, and the geographical and ecological attributes of plants. Alongside the new taxonomy there has been timely and devoted application to study of the floras of those great regions of the world, at once brought closer and jeopardized by modern transport: there are in publication accounts of the great floras of the Congo, Angola, Madagascar, East Africa, the Zambezi basin, the Arctic, Soviet Russia and the Malayan region.

The study of plant geography has been encouraged by the growth of pollen analysis, which has provided a strikingly consistent picture of climatic and vegetational changes throughout interglacial periods, the glaciations and the present post-glacial time. In conjunction with geological and archaeological indices, we have thus been provided with factual knowledge of the whereabouts of our flora through the vicissitudes of at least the past million years, and this form of micro-palaeontology is now being applied with the greatest effect to the stratigraphy of Tertiary and earlier deposits, where on the one hand it is a major prop to oil prospecting and on the other offers contribution to solution of such basic problems as that of continental drift.

A development of the greatest significance has been the acknowledgment of the validity and importance of the ecological approach to the study of plant life—what may be termed scientific natural history. Journals and societies devoted to ecology have arisen in all parts of the world, and in Britain the foundation of the Nature Conservancy has underlined the importance of investigating our natural resources of vegetation, soil and animal life. Not only do we thereby learn the principles of conservation of invaluable native assets. but we foster a " holistic " approach to study of the plant, that already has deeply affected both agriculture and forestry.

IV—More Light on the Genes

By Kenneth Mather, C.B.E., F.R.S.
Professor of Genetics, University of Birmingham

AS a science, genetics is as old as the century. The first 30 years or so saw it chiefly concerned with working out the mechanism of hereditary transmission from parent to offspring. This clearly demonstrated that the genes are borne by the chromosomes which themselves form part of the nucleus to be found in virtually every living cell. This raised two great questions: of the chemical nature of these genetically all-important chromosomes, and of how their genes control the living processes of the cell.

The way in which genes do their work has been studied embryologically, chiefly in mammals and flies, and biochemically especially in micro-organisms. The embryological studies have shown how a single initial effect of the gene can be built up in the ramifications of development to produce a most complex and often surprising constellation of consequences in the adult animal. The biochemical studies have been concerned more with the process going on inside the cell and

have shown how the production of amino-acids, vitamins and other essentials of life is controlled by series of genes acting stepwise through the agency of enzymes each taking the product of its predecessor's action as a raw material and amplifying it in a specific way. Most of these processes go on in the cytoplasm—the living material in which the nucleus with its chromosomes and genes is embedded. Electron microscopy is revealing the structure of this cytoplasm, while genetical experimentation is beginning to show us how it acts as the agent of the genes and by its consequent changes gives rise to the many types of cell found within the bodies of animals and plants.

One of the greatest steps forward in our understanding of the nature of the genetic materials themselves has been their identification with deoxyribose nucleic acid (D.N.A.) which forms giant molecules arranged as a pair of spiral chains linked together by organic bases. These links are of four kinds, and it seems almost certain

99

that the genetical information is coded into the D.N.A. by the way they succeed one another along the chains.

Genetical studies of the fine structure of chromosomes are proceeding too, especially with microorganisms, in which it is easy to raise the vast numbers of individuals required for such work. This approach is showing how the spatial arrangement of materials within the chromosome determines genetic action just as would be expected from the chemical structure, and we may look forward with some confidence to the final link being forged between chemical structure and genetic action. Then will come the question of how this genetical information, coded into the D.N.A., is decoded to be expressed in the biochemical processes of the cell. This we do not yet know, but we already have a clue from the discovery that certain single gene changes in man express themselves by altering specific amino-acids in haemoglobin, the characteristic protein of blood cells.

While digging deeper into the cell and its processes, genetics has also been concerned at the other end of the scale with the behaviour of populations of animals and plants. The occurrence and nature of genetical variation in wild populations has been made clear and the action of natural selection in moulding them to the requirements of the environment firmly established in plants, animals and man. Genetical findings have not merely under-pinned Darwin's theory of evolution by natural selection, but have given us a new picture of populations as held in dynamic equilibrium by the forces of selection, and inevitably changing if these forces are altered or new variation introduced. This has been demonstrated in man, where genes that upset the haemoglobin will in one condition produce anaemia but in another confer resistance to malaria.

Variation in man is now being intensively explored by a variety of methods. New genically determined biochemical differences are coming to light as well as abnormalities in the number of chromosomes, normally constant at 46 in man, which have been shown to produce gross upsets both physical and mental. The origin of new genic variants by mutation is important, too, in the assessment of hazards arising from exposure to radiations, which are known to stimulate at least some forms of genetic change.

Methods of assessing and analysing genetic variation, especially in characteristics like stature and I.Q. in man that grade smoothly between wide extremes, have been greatly developed in the past decade or so. They promise further to extend our understanding of human populations, and are even now being applied in the refinement of techniques for the improvement of domestic plants and animals. This is perhaps a less spectacular development of genetics, but one that promises to be of great significance for man and his food supplies.

V—Mathematics made Easy

By M. V. Wilkes, F.R.S.
President, British Computer Society

THE digital computer is only 16 years old—that is, if one leaves out of account the early work of Charles Babbage, who tried to do with steam and cog wheels what is now done with electricity and transistors. Some pioneering work was done during the later stages of the Second World War, but it was not until the war was over that the development of digital computers started in earnest. By the end of 1949 a handful of powerful computers of the modern stored-programme type were working. Since then development has gone ahead at breakneck speed, and the digital computer is now commonplace in laboratories and offices.

In scientific research, digital computers have been in use long enough for their influence to be felt in many branches of science, and each succeeding volume of the Proceedings of the Royal Society to come out contains at least one report of work done with their aid. The goal envisaged by the digital computer pioneers was nothing less than the freeing of theoretical science from the straitjacket imposed by the purely technical difficulties of traditional mathematics. It is easy enough to write down mathematical equations; but, as every schoolboy knows, solving them is another matter. The potential power of numerical mathematics to break this deadlock had long been appreciated, and all that was wanted was the development of powerful enough computing machines. Modern machines will do in a few minutes what would take a man unaided a lifetime, and computations are now regularly planned and executed on a scale that would have been inconceivable a few years ago. I believe, however, that even the biggest and fastest machines at present available are too small for us to have experienced anything more than the bare beginnings of what we can confidently expect.

Fortunately, machine designers have not been idle, and new machines that will be faster and free from many of the limitations of existing machines are under active development. An outstanding project in this country is the Atlas computer being developed at Manchester University, which will be produced commercially. If Atlas computers become widely available to research workers in universities and elsewhere, I am convinced that they will make possible spectacular advances in many subjects, from nuclear and atomic physics on the one hand to crystal structure and molecular biology on the other.

Although there will be plenty for the next generation of digital computers to do, some people are already beginning to think about the next generation but one. It is much to be hoped that the means will be found whereby this country can play a leading part in the development of the very advanced techniques necessary. It must be remembered that every pound spent on digital computer development

Modern Computers.—A compact stored-programme computor, made by IBM United Kingdom Ltd.

An electronic data processing machine.

will in the not too distant future pay dividends over a whole range of science and technology. It would be folly to support scientific and technical research on a large scale, but to neglect the basic tools such as computers.

It must not be thought that it is only scientists and engineers who have need for very large and fast calculating machines. There is also the field known as operational research, which includes problems in scheduling and allocation. Already many firms with a transport or distribution problem have found that they can make savings by calling in the aid of a digital computer. A mathematical method known as " linear programming " enables straight-forward jobs to be dealt with on an ordinary sized computer, but the more complicated problems generally require methods involving a measure of trial and error, and these can make great demands on computer speed. At present most really interesting problems are beyond the range of existing computers. It may well turn out that operational research will be the field of application in which the new very fast machines will have their greatest direct economic significance.

VI—Handmaiden of Many Sciences

By Sir Robert Robinson, O.M., F.R.S.

Emeritus Professor of Chemistry, University of Oxford

THE elaboration of the system of organic chemistry, one of the greatest of human achievements, occupied little more than the last third of the life of the Royal Society. It was rendered possible by the recognition of very simple rules governing the mode of linking of atoms in the molecules of the multitude of carbon compounds.

The development, having an almost mathematical precision, was very satisfying within its limits and there was no dearth of problems; for example, those set by nature, the complex substances produced by plants and animals. The routine sequence was first, isolation and purification; secondly, determination of the molecular structure; and thirdly, confirmation by chemical synthesis. A classical example was Baeyer's work on indigo. In establishing the architecture of the molecule and later, in finding out how to build it, quite new regions of chemistry were discovered and explored. Later the commercial aspect was involved, and the production of artificial indigo by the chemical industry was not only a triumph in itself but led to a surprising number of associated technological advances.

Gaining experience and craft, the organic chemist analysed and synthesized more and more complex molecules; some of the milestones along the road were glucose, camphor, nicotine, atropine, the blood pigment, and cholesterol. During the present century the rate of acceleration of progress has continuously increased so that at the present time, with certain exceptions, the molecular structure of the entire range of natural products, so far isolated, is known at least to such an extent that a conspectus of the whole has been gained.

Furthermore, synthesis has reached new heights exemplified by the laboratory preparation of morphine (Gates), oxytocin —a complex polypeptide hormone of the pituitary (du Vigneaud), strychnine, reserpine and, it is rumoured, of chlorophyll (Woodward). These and other brilliant achievements of the American schools

First year organic chemistry students at work in the laboratory.

were the outcome of a great concentration of effort and well organized, unfettered team work. It certainly seems that any molecular structure can be erected provided the attack is pressed hard enough, long enough and with resources adequate to the task.

This happy position is partly the result of the discovery of new, generally applicable molecular building processes but it is also due to a better understanding of the circumstances controlling the occurrence and direction of chemical change. Until comparatively recently our objective in synthesis was to construct a molecule in which the mode of linking of the atoms corresponded to the graphical formula set down on paper. But this is in two dimensions and the molecules exist in space of three dimensions. A simple example will serve to show that this introduces dubieties. Suppose, for instance, we have a ring of five carbon atoms numbered 1, 2, 3, 4, 5, and we can add two carbon atoms (with associated atoms), one to position - 1 and the second to position - 2. We already know that the five carbon atoms of the ring lie in a plane and that

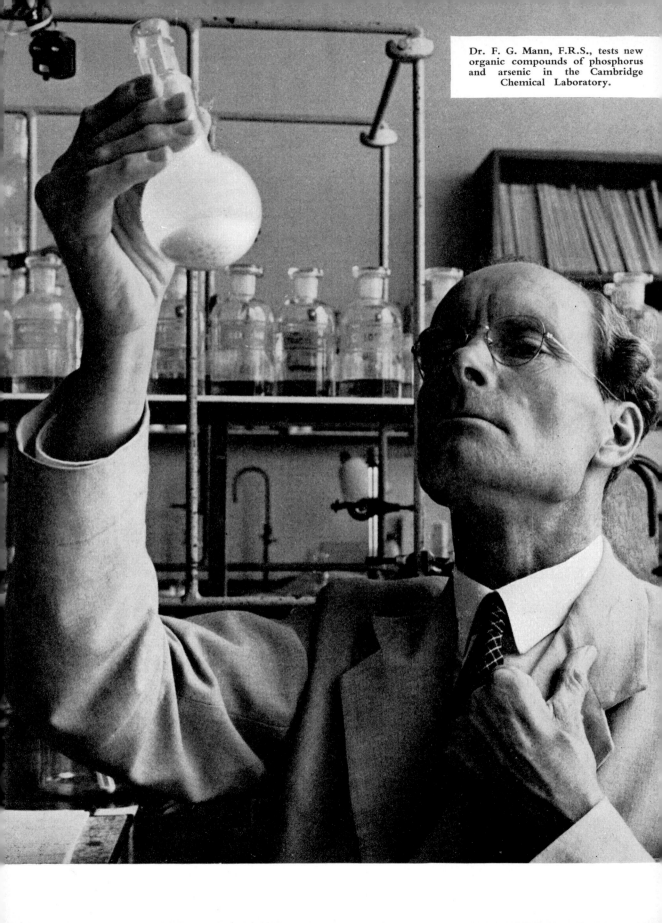

Dr. F. G. Mann, F.R.S., tests new organic compounds of phosphorus and arsenic in the Cambridge Chemical Laboratory.

atoms joined to these ring carbons will lie above or below that plane. It is therefore possible for the two atoms we add to the ring carbons 1 and 2 to go both to the same side of the ring, or one to one side and the second to the other. The resulting molecules are quite different. The science of arrangement of atoms in space in this and similar senses is called stereo-chemistry, and the past decade has seen the emergence of various stereospecific syntheses. This new power has been gained, not only by the extended study of reaction processes, but also of the principles governing their orientation and of the stereochemical influences affecting the course of chemical change. This latter aspect of discovery and endeavour in organic chemistry has only comparatively recently assumed its undoubted great importance.

The dramatic advances of recent years (even in the past decade) were naturally made possible by the work of earlier pioneers, but certain developments were of special significance. First, there was the introduction of micro-analysis and micro-manipulation; the saving of time and labour was of enormous value. Secondly, the elaboration of new methods of separation or purification of substances. The most generally useful of these is the so-called chromatography in its various modifications, which is based on selective adsorption on surfaces. The operation is routine in organic chemical laboratories and, armed with this weapon, Sanger was able, for the first time, to demonstrate the full constitution of a protein, namely insulin, a most outstanding achievement and one that was thought beyond reach not so many years ago.

Other methods of separation of great value are electrophoresis, ultra-centrifugation and counter-current partition between partly immiscible solvents, and variants of the method.

Thirdly, the use of physical methods for the study of molecular structure has made giant strides. The first generally used method was the measurement of light absorption in the ultra-violet region. This gives much information and is not superseded by other methods, which are complementary to it. Measurement of absorption in the infra-red is a more additively constitutive property, and the observed results are due to comparatively simple groups in the molecule. Recently, the measurement of nuclear magnetic resonance and electron spin resonance has had notable successes, even in assisting the determination of complex structures such as those of certain alkaloids that had resisted more conventional attack. A more direct method is that of X-ray crystallography, which is rapidly becoming not merely a necessary resource, but even the only resource that is necessary. This position has not yet been reached, but we are well on the way to it.

Very significant recent results are the establishment of the structures of Vitamin

B^{12} (Crowfoot-Hodgkin), of deoxyribonucleic acid and of haemoglobin (Perutz). In all these cases the work was supplementary to the results of chemical degradation (Sir Alexander Todd and collaborators on B^{12}), but the information gained was more precise, particularly in the stereochemical field. Already we hear of relations between the chemical constitution of the proteins and hereditary factors.

Undoubtedly the progress of the past few years in these branches of the science is of the utmost significance, and it is here that the most rapid advances can be confidently anticipated. On the industrial side, the main progress has been in the production of new macromolecular substances, often by the polymerization of simple units. Ziegler introduced a new method of polymerizing ethylene (a C_2 unit), and in view of the preceding remarks it is of interest to note that Natta adapted the Ziegler process so as to effect stereospecific polymerization of propylene (a C_3 unit).

Organic chemistry is the handmaiden of many other sciences, especially medicine and agriculture. Recent developments in these directions have been numerous and important, but may be considered more appropriately in relation to those disciplines.

VII—What Constitutes Life?

By Sir Lawrence Bragg, O.B.E., F.R.S.
Fullerian Professor of Chemistry, Royal Institution

I MAY perhaps begin by explaining what the formidable looking expression molecular biology means. It represents a new approach to the problem of trying to understand how living matter works; recent achievements of science have made it possible to get detailed knowledge of its structure on a much finer scale than hitherto, in fact right down to the scale when we are beginning to see how its atoms are arranged.

There have been two main ways of studying the structure of the living body, by the microscope and by chemical analysis. The microscope makes it possible to see details some thousands of times finer than can be discerned by the naked eye. The smallest lump of matter that can be seen under a microscope, however, is still some thousands of atoms across, and so contains thousands of millions of atoms. The microscope is a very long way from telling us how the atoms are arranged; it is as if it only gave us a map of England showing where the towns are, while we want to find out something about the people who live in them. Chemistry tells us of what kinds of chemical compounds the body is built. The atoms are for the most part carbon, oxygen, nitrogen and hydrogen, with a small proportion of other elements such as sulphur and phosphorus that have a key part in the structures, and a minute proportion of " trace elements " that are needed only for certain special purposes but are still essential for life. Chemistry can break down the substances of living matter into recognizable fragments of groups of atoms or molecules, and deduce how they are joined together by chemical bonds. It can isolate large molecules that take part in the chemical processes of the body and get some idea of their function.

The new advances have resulted from the development of two new techniques. The electron microscope, which uses a beam of electrons instead of light, has immensely increased the power of seeing fine details. It is as much more powerful

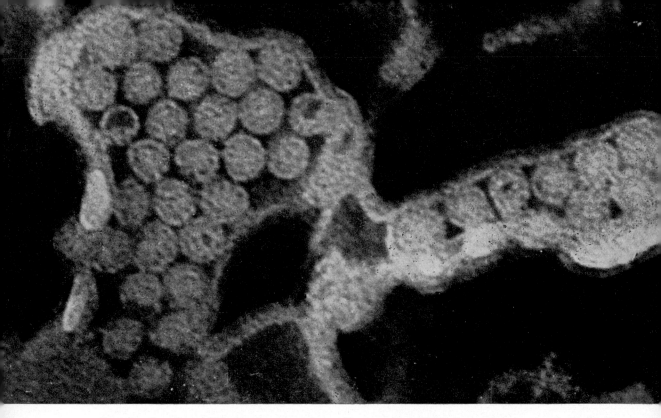

Particles of a poliomyelitis virus in a stage of assembly, magnified 400,000 times.   From a paper by R. W. Horne and J. Naginton in the *Journal of Molecular Biology*.

than the light microscope as the latter is compared with the unaided eye. One can distinguish elements of structure only some tens of atoms across and so containing merely thousands of atoms. X-ray analysis studies the arrangements of atoms in bodies by observing the way they scatter X-rays. The many different kinds of chemical compound are built of molecules, the molecules of each kind of compound being small groups of atoms joined in a definite way. X-ray analysis started 50 years ago to find out the exact positions of atoms in molecules, at first in the very simplest kinds with only a few atoms. As the techniques improved, it has become more and more powerful, successfully

analysing molecules like penicillin with 100 or so atoms in them. Quite recently it has succeeded in analysing all the atomic positions in large molecules containing thousands of atoms.

The exciting and very important stage has thus been reached when there is a completed bridge between the techniques. The electron microscope has attained such a resolution that one can " see " (in photographs) details of structures containing thousands of atoms; and X-ray analysis, approaching the problem from the other end, has reached a stage when we can learn from it how the atoms are arranged in bits of structure of this size. For the first time we are beginning to be able to read the whole story, from the atoms upwards.

It is only possible here to give the briefest indication of the kind of new knowledge that is being gained. We have already learnt much more about the most important constituents of living matter. All living matter consists of cells; the simplest organisms are just one cell, more complicated ones are masses of cells of different kinds which have different functions in the body. The cell, inside its envelope, is mainly composed of protein, large molecules of many different kinds containing thousands of atoms, each of which has a definite function in the chemical processes taking place in the living cell. Inside this mass of protein is the nucleus, which appears to be the seat of the hereditary character. It is, as it were, a little book of instructions inside the cell telling it how it should be made up. Growth takes place by cells dividing into two, and when this happens the nucleus of the mother cell somehow prints off copies of this book of instructions, one going to each daughter cell. The atomic arrangement in the nucleic acid, the long chain compound that contains this code of instructions, was deduced a few years ago by Crick and Watson at Cambridge, and the fascinating feature of their solution is that it gives a hint how the one code is turned into two, that is, how heredity is handed on. The nucleic acid is made of two intertwined chains of atoms of a complementary kind, like the wards of a key and of the lock into which it fits. In duplication the chains come apart, and as it were each key picks up the right bits to form another lock, and each lock to form another key, so that we have two sets of instructions in place of one

Recently, Perutz and Kendrew, with their collaborators, have succeeded in making the first analysis of one type of protein molecule and many more kinds will no doubt follow. On the one hand we have a blueprint of the molecule to help in explaining how it performs its chemical tasks; on the other it may be hoped that it will explain how the nucleic acid acts as a template to make protein molecules. The elements of the code mechanism are quite simple, but in a higher form of life like a mammal there are thousands of millions of them in the tiny nucleus; if they were letters of books they would fill a large library.

It is not possible to mention in so short an article the names of the many workers who have made these new advances; our own country has played a large part in exploring this fascinating new field of science.

VIII—Nuclear Excitements

By Sir John Cockcroft, O.M., K.C.B., F.R.S.
Master of Churchill College, Cambridge

DURING the past decade the pace of discovery in nuclear physics has shown no sign of slackening, and high energy nuclear physics is today one of the most important growing points of science.

The triumphantly successful proton synchrotron at the European Organization for Nuclear Research (CERN) has pushed the range of artificially accelerated projectiles available for experiment up to 28,000 million volts. Beyond this, in the cosmic rays, physicists have available nuclear particles much fewer in number but with 10,000 times higher energy.

In the collision of these very energetic nuclei new transient forms of matter are produced. The first of these to be discovered were the mesons. The pimesons, 280 times as heavy as electrons, are considered to play a dominant part in binding together protons and neutrons in the atomic nucleus. The pimesons created in nuclear collisions decay into mu-mesons 215 times as heavy as electrons, and these

in turn decay into electrons and neutrinos. In more energetic collisions a group of particles known to physicists as "strange particles" are produced. There are three kinds of K mesons, having positive, negative, or no charge, about three times as heavy as the pi-mesons. These can break up in an interesting variety of ways into lighter particles. Beyond the K mesons are the hyperons, which are heavier than protons and which decay into protons and pi-mesons, neutrons and pi-mesons, or into other lighter members of the hyperon family.

Most of these nuclear particles have associated with them so-called anti-particles. When a particle meets its anti-particle they annihilate each other and energy is released either in the form of lighter particles or radiation. The existence of anti-particles was predicted by Dirac over 30 years ago, and the first to be discovered was the positive electron. The production of anti-protons was demonstrated in the giant bevatron at Berkeley, and protons and anti-

112

protons were seen to anihilate each other with the production of showers of mesons.

Since then other anti-particles have been found. Particles and anti-particles have the same mass and lifetimes but opposite charge and magnetic properties. Anti-matter cannot be stored in our own galaxy, but it is an interesting subject for after-dinner speculation whether other galaxies might be composed of anti-matter. In this case the collision of galaxies could lead to very exciting nuclear fireworks.

The family of sub-atomic particles is believed to be limited in number, and theoretical physicists have invented rules to explain this family limitation, though they are far from explaining why they have their individual masses and why they behave in such a strange way. This behaviour must be intimately related to the nature of the nuclear forces which bind matter together.

The study of the methods of decay of K mesons led to the remarkable discovery that sub-atomic particles ejected from nuclei spin like tops, but only in one direction. Processes of this kind had been previously assumed to be symmetrical, anti-

Some of the 100 magnet blocks of the world's biggest " atom smasher ", the 28,000 million electron-volt proton synchrotron at the CERN site near Geneva, which was inaugurated in 1960.

7 GeV PROTON SYNCHROTO

Plan of the 7,000 million electron-volt proton synchrotron being built at the National Institute of Nuclear Science.

clockwise rotation being as inherently probable as clockwise. But no physicist had checked to see; when they did, these processes of nature were found to be asymmetric.

The successful operation of the CERN 28,000 million volt proton synthrotron has shown already that very large numbers of anti-protons are produced in collisions —far more than had been anticipated. Experimentalists are already looking to see whether any new and stranger particles are produced in the collisions. Very unexpectedly they have already found that

when the 28,000 million volt protons bombarded an aluminium foil, nuclei of heavy hydrogen were knocked out sideways—a most surprising result for why should a neutron and proton come out of such a violent impact joined together?

Compared with this succession of new discoveries in high energy nuclear physics, the classical low energy nuclear physics, which was born in the 1930s, may now seem less exciting. Nevertheless we are continuing to learn a great deal about the detailed structure of the complex atomic nuclei, containing as they do up to 250 neutrons and protons bound together by the nuclear forces, rotating and vibrating in numerous modes that are now being unravelled.

The giant electron linear accelerator at Stanford on the Californian coast is being used to explore the internal structure of the protons and neutrons themselves. Already some form of structure seems to be showing up and it will be interesting to see how much further detail is revealed as higher and higher energy electrons become available for this purpose.

IX—Below Earth's Crust

By L. R. Wager, F.R.S.
Professor of Geology, University of Oxford

GEOCHEMISTRY developed into a coherent part of science between the wars largely through the work of V. M. Goldschmidt, who defined its primary purpose: "to determine quantitatively the composition of the earth and its parts and . . . to discover the laws which control the distribution of the individual elements". As in all geology there is an historical aspect, and the geochemist is also concerned with the changes in the distribution of elements in the earth during geological time.

Surveys of the distribution of most chemical elements in the chief minerals and rocks of the earth's crust and in the ocean and atmosphere have now been made. The amount of an element in any particular unit of the earth is the result of geological processes, such as weathering, sedimentation, magmatic differentiation, metasomatism, &c. The geochemist is particularly trying to understand these complex processes by means of his chemical data, and in acquiring this he is being greatly helped by new techniques of analysis such as the isotope dilution and radioactivation methods.

Most natural elements are mixtures of several isotopes, and during the past decade a completely new field of geochemistry has been opened up by mass spectrometric determinations of the proportions of the natural isotopes in the different kinds of terrestrial materials. It has been shown that for certain of the lighter elements significant isotopic in the I.G.Y. in 1954 it was learnt that fractionation has occurred. For example, the ratio of oxygen-18 to oxygen-16 has been found to vary, the lowest ratio observed being for polar ice and the highest for atmospheric carbon dioxide; these differences are the result of distillation processes and chemical reactions. On the other hand, variations in the ratio of the stable carbon isotopes C-12 and C-13 are traceable to biological processes. Smudges of carbon in the rocks that cannot possibly be recognised as fossils can be proved organic in origin by the isotope ratios; in this way it should ultimately be possible to decide at what stage in the history of the earth living organisms were evolved. Sulphur isotope ratios are also changed by organic agencies, in this case by sulphate reducing bacteria, and sulphur, labelled as it were by the bacteria, may sometimes be kept an eye on during subsequent geological migrations.

The geochemistry of certain radioactive isotopes produced by cosmic radiation in the upper atmosphere, and of others produced by nuclear explosions, have especial interest. Thus radioactive carbon-14 is produced by cosmic rays in very small quantities, and some is taken up by plants during growth. This isotope decays slowly so that the amount remaining in ancient plant material can be used to estimate the time that has elapsed since the carbon was incorporated in it; in this way fossil wood is being dated back to about 60,000 years. Tritium (^{3}H) is also being continuously produced in the upper atmosphere; there it combines to form water and then enters the ordinary water cycle. The total amount of terrestrial tritium is estimated as only 100 lb.; but its presence can be detected and measured by extremely sensitive radioactive counters and it is being used to trace the larger circulatory movements of the oceans and atmosphere.

For elements that are decaying by natural radioactivity the abundance of a daughter element relative to the parent in a particular mineral or rock provides a measure of its absolute age. Determinations of age are being made by the decay of uranium and thorium to lead, of potassium-40 to argon-40, and of rubidium-87 to strontium-87. The very small quantities of the radioactively produced elements are often determined by the isotope dilution method, recently made possible by refinements in mass spectrometry and the availability of specially prepared concentrates of stable isotopes. For the rubidium/strontium age method the amount of the radiogenic strontium in mica may be determined within approximately 2 per cent. at a level of about one part per million, and ages of rocks, in favourable circumstances, are believed to be known within 3 or 4 per cent. The period of time for which there is a detailed fossil record has been established by these methods as about 600 million years, but Pre-Cambrian time, during which ordinary geological processes such as erosion and sedimentation were taking place, stretches back at least to 3,500 million years. By comparing the isotope ratios of lead from iron meteorites and from present-day oceanic sediments, the time since the material of the earth became distinct from the rest of the solar system has been estimated as 4,500 million years.

The available materials at or near the surface of the earth are being subjected to more and more detailed analyses, but the material deep in the earth is at present out of reach. As a result of rather indirect lines of evidence there is considerable confidence in the view that beneath the crust there is a mantle of mainly magnesium silicate rock and below this a metallic, iron-nickel core. Knowledge about the overall composition of our plant will be taken a great step forward when, as is now planned, a hole is drilled to a depth of seven or eight miles and the geochemist can investigate actual samples of what lies beneath the crust.

X—I.G.Y.—and More to Come

By Sydney Chapman, F.R.S.

Visiting Professor of Geophysics, University of Alaska

THE International Geophysical Year of 1957-58, commonly known as the I.G.Y., greatly enriched our store of observations of a wide range of physical aspects of our planet. This material is now being actively studied, and such studies must continue for some years to gather the full fruits of this immense enterprise. But some striking discoveries came quickly to light. An example is the great submarine river that flows eastward for at least 3,500 miles near the Equator in the Pacific Ocean. In volume it rivals the Gulf Stream, with a current 250 miles wide and from 100 to 800 ft. below the surface. Above and below it are two weaker counter-currents.

But the most striking and unexpected recent geophysical discoveries relate to the regions above the earth's surface. Since the end of the Second World War rocket researches into the upper atmosphere had been made in the United States with increasing success. Little was known of Russian progress in this field. In formulating the plans for the I.G.Y. a considerable extension of such rocket researches was foreseen from the outset. After the Soviet Union joined in the I.G.Y. in 1954, it was learnt that they would include such researches in their programme. Other nations also took part in it to a much smaller degree.

In 1954, at the instance of the young American physicist Singer, the launching of earth satellites for scientific research was included in the I.G.Y. programme. In 1955 the United States, and in 1956 the Soviet Union, announced that their national I.G.Y. programme would include such launchings. In 1955 the symbol adopted for the I.G.Y. included a satellite and its orbit round the earth. This was a venture of faith, not unmingled with doubt. The first three months of the I.G.Y. passed and no satellite had been launched.

Then came the massive Russian satellites, three in all, and the smaller but scientifically successful American satellites. The ability

119

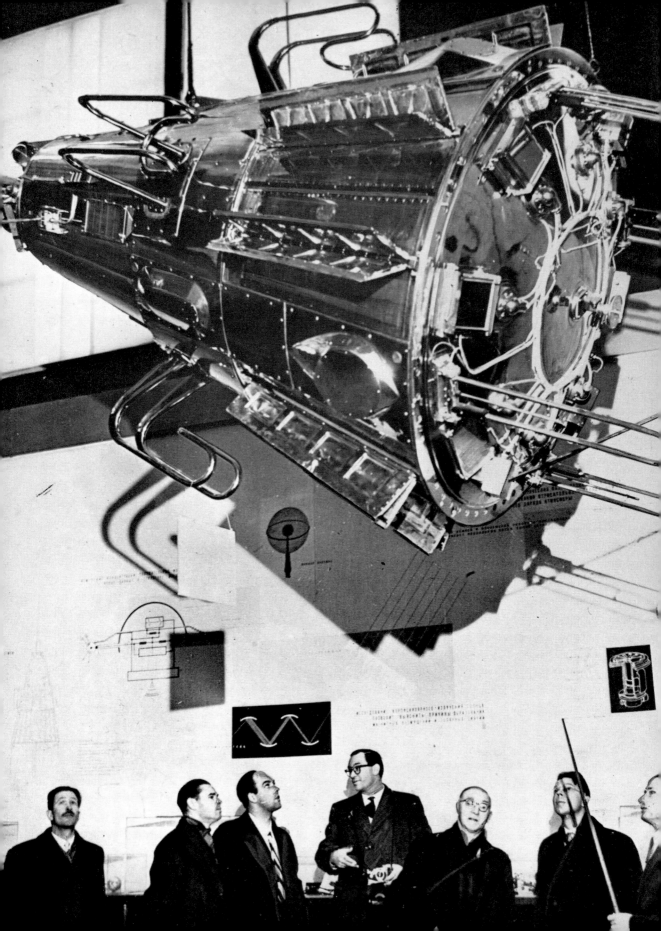

to launch and guide such missiles was soon used by both nations to launch cosmic rockets. Whereas the regular I.G.Y. rocket programme was designed to explore the earth's atmosphere up to a few hundred miles at most—itself a great technical achievement—the cosmic rockets travelled immensely farther. Their orbits extended far beyond those of the satellites, and even to and beyond the moon. Britain launched no satellites and cosmic rockets. But happily she was able to play a notable part in this programme through the work of the great radio-telescope at Jodrell Bank. This had exceptional capacity to follow their motions and to receive their signals.

The satellites and cosmic rockets revealed that, like Saturn, the earth has external appendages—the belts now associated with the names of the American scientist Van Allen and the Russian scientist Vernov, who with their colleagues took the leading part in this remarkable discovery and exploration. Unlike Saturn's rings these belts are not visible, nor confined to a thin plane layer, nor apparently constant, nor composed of dust and larger particles. They extend over a volume far greater than that of the solid and liquid earth. They consist of electrons and atomic nuclei—mainly protons—moving with great speed. These particles form a distinct assemblage of gas of extremely low density, in the midst of air also very rare, but relatively far denser. The form of the belts and the motions of their particles are governed mainly by the field of the obliquely magnetized earth.

The outer belt extends at times outwards to 10 times the earth's radius from the earth's centre. Its extent and intensity vary considerably from time to time. It tends to decay by dispersion of its particles into our atmosphere. It is generally believed to be renewed and maintained by the addition of gas coming from disturbed regions on the sun. It is not yet known how the earth by its magnetic field is able to capture some of this gas.

The particles of the belts spiral round the lines of geomagnetic force between arctic and antarctic latitudes. They also drift round the earth, the electrons eastward and the nuclei westward. A westward electric current is associated with the belts. This produces a distortion of the geomagnetic field at a distance of a few earth radii, which has been observed by cosmic rockets. One of these also showed that the moon is substantially non-magnetic. The dark side of the moon was photographed.

These remarkable technical and scientific advances are a foretaste of greater discoveries to come. They will lead on to a new era in the history of mankind, for good or ill.

121

British physicists invited by the Russians to view a replica of the third sputnik in the Pavilion of the Academy of Sciences, Moscow.

XI—Experiments in Space

By Sir Harrie Massey, F.R.S.
Quain Professor of Physics, University College, London

WHEN, towards the end of 1946, the Americans launched a V2 rocket containing scientific equipment, nearly vertically so that it attained an altitude of about 60 miles, space research was born. In the period of less than 14 years that has elapsed since that occasion, the advances made in the technique of rocket propulsion and guidance have been very great indeed, so great that they have tended to overshadow the scientific results that have been obtained. This is not surprising when one thinks of the launching of artificial planets, an actual direct hit on the moon, facsimile transmission from 200,000 miles distance of a photograph of the back of the moon, and command signals effective in switching on equipment in a vehicle at several million miles distance. On the other hand, the possibilities opened for scientific research by the development of these techniques are unlimited and will not be sorted out for generations to come.

There is a very great deal to be studied in the earth's atmosphere at altitudes far above that attainable by balloons (about 20 miles) and we have the opportunity of exploring the universe from outside the atmosphere, so that we are no longer restricted to viewing the sun and the heavenly bodies in visible light and a narrow band of radio waves. We may now look forward to the development of ultra-violet, X-ray, and infra-red astronomy, in which the radiation in these wavelengths, screened off from us on the ground by our atmosphere, is the subject of study. Specially interesting to us on earth is the additional scope afforded for investigating the ways in which the sun influences our atmosphere to produce weather, climate, and many upper atmospheric phenomena, including the normal and disturbed ionosphere, the polar aurorae and magnetic storms. We also can gain information about the solid structure of our planet. The prospect of detailed study of

Launching a Skylark research rocket at Woomera.

British scientists at Burlington House after the launching of the first Russian satellite. On the left, at the globe, is Dr. R. Woolley, the Astronomer Royal, and behind him from left to right are Professor Martin Ryle, Dr. R. L. Smith-Rose, Sir Owen Wansbrough-Jones and Mr. J. A. Ratcliffe.

the moon and the nearer planets is open before us. In this connexion, there is also the exciting possibility of obtaining more insight into the nature of life from biological observations on Mars and Venus. Furthermore, all this programme can be carried out with automatic equipment alone.

As an example of ultra-violet and X-ray astronomy we may cite the observations of the intensity of these radiations from the sun that have been made, using instruments taken up in vertical sounding rockets. It has been found that the sun emits X-rays in much greater intensity than would be expected from the temperature of the visible disc. The first observation of the emission of ultra-violet light from the northern sky was made in 1957 in the United States and showed that many of the regions that show up most strongly in this light do not appear on a photograph in visible light. This is a foretaste of the new discoveries likely to be made when this type of research develops.

Much new information of importance has been obtained about the structure of the atmosphere, the nature and properties of the ionosphere and the figure of the earth. The greatest discoveries, however, have concerned so-called particle radiation. It has been found that in two great regions surrounding the earth there is a concentration of energetic charged particles greater than anticipated. The inner region is centred at a distance of about 1,000 miles from the earth, the outer at 15,000 miles or so. In both zones the concentration is built up by the effect of the earth's magnetic field in trapping the charged particles. The possibility of this trapping was demonstrated in three remarkable experiments, carried out by the United States, in which, on each occasion, an artificial radiation belt was created between the two natural regions by exploding an atom bomb at a nominal height of 400 miles above the South Atlantic. The artificial belts, over 50 miles thick, were detectable for five days or so. The successful prosecution of these cosmic experiments is a sufficient indication of the very advanced state now reached in space research.

The British Skylark rocket rose to a record height of 138 miles. These 25 ft. rockets carried American instruments to gather information about the upper atmosphere. ▶

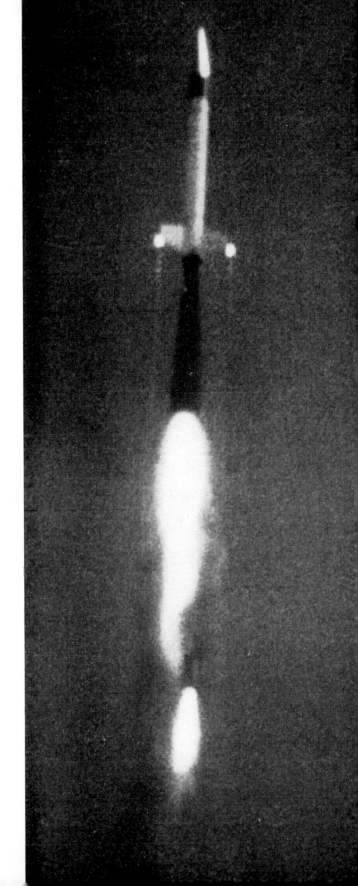

XII—Ploughing Deep into Abstract Theory

By G. Temple, C.B.E., F.R.S.

Sedleian Professor of Natural Philosophy, University of Oxford

IN pure mathematics the oustanding recent event has been the series of publications by an anonymous group of French mathematicians writing under the pseudonym of "Bourbaki". In brief, these monographs are designed to do for mathematics what the Académie Française does for the French language, or what the Code Napoléon did for French law—namely, to establish a final and definitive terminology and a magisterial order of development made as general, and therefore as abstract, as recent research will permit. In time, all pure mathematics will be subsumed under this splendid effort of codification; its main effort so far has been in algebra, topology, and analysis.

Of these topics the most exciting and rapidly developing has undoubtedly been topology, which may be crudely described as the study of those geometrical properties that are unaffected by any continuous deformation. The highly abstract character of modern topological research makes it almost impossible to describe in ordinary language, but even the applied mathematician receives with gratitude the very general, most powerful and widely applicable theorems on the fixed points of mappings in function spaces.

The developments in algebra may be exemplified by the profound and fruitful investigations on the structure of Lie groups, which have transformed the pioneering work buried in the weighty tomes of Marius Sophus Lie into a rich and penetrating study in which algebra, analysis, and topology play closely integrated roles.

In the field of geometry, understood in its widest sense, some outstanding marks of recent developments are the explicit consideration of the topological characteristics of the " space " under consideration and of global rather than local properties. This is especially evident in the calculus of variations now studied "in the large" rather than in the narrow confines of small variations.

Finally, it is imperative to mention the important progress that is being made in transforming the theory of probability and stochastic processes in bringing powerful topological tools to bear on the theory of ordinary and partial differential equations and in the creation of the theory of distributions and generalized functions, which has justified the intuitions of the physicist and engineer.

The study of applied mathematics is being transformed by a systematic use of high-speed computing machinery, which has often converted the existence theorems of the analyst into effective programmes for effective numerical calculations and has rendered obsolete the old distinction between "soluble" and "insoluble" problems. Even classical mechanics has attracted new interest from the problems posed by artificial satellites and by the beginnings of the exploration of outer space.

Leaving on one side such investigations as the quantum theory of fields, nuclear theory, and the study of the thirty-odd strange elementary particles (which belong rather to theoretical physics), the advances in applied mathematics can be illustrated from the mechanics of continua, whether solid, liquid, or gaseous. The theory of elasticity has now been extended to deal with problems of plasticity, of large deformation, and of the strange materials that form the subject matter of rheology. Fluid dynamics no longer means the study of the perfect fluid, but includes the effects of turbulence, compressibility, viscosity, and thermal conduction in real gases, under extreme conditions of high temperature, low pressure, ionisation, and dissociation. Particular mention must be made of the new science of magneto-hydrodynamics, which studies the motion of conducting media in electromagnetic fields, whether in a shock tube, a plasma, a mercury turbine, or on the vast cosmic scale of intergalactic clouds. Here, applied mathematics shades off into the kinetic theory of gases and joins forces with theoretical chemistry and astrophysics.

This short and selective catalogue can do little more than illustrate the extraordinary expansion of mathematics in recent times, the wide fields that it is bringing under cultivation, and the depth of the ploughing into abstract theory that is its indispensable prerequisite.

XIII—Basic Patterns of Life

By D. R. Wilkie

HOW is progress in physiology to be measured? Our fundamental aim—to understand the phenomena of life in terms of ordinary chemistry and physics—is reflected by a sub-division of the subject into biochemistry and biophysics. And at last we are beginning to make out some of the basic functional patterns that recur throughout the complex multitude of living things.

Physiology is increasingly concerned with single cells, or even with single molecules within the cell. This is largely a consequence of the emergence of new experimental techniques of unprecedented sensitivity.

Life, even of the simplest kind, has not yet been created in the laboratory; but the gap between living and non-living things is visibly dwindling. The simplest viruses are now known to be composed of nothing but a core of nucleic acid wrapped around with protein. Moreover, it has been shown that a mixture of ordinary chemicals—water, methane and ammonia—supplied with energy, generates significant quantities of several materials that are characteristic of living things: such as amino-acids—the building blocks from which proteins are constructed.

The investigation of chemical problems has been transformed by the technique of chromatography, which makes it possible to separate and identify minute quantities of chemical substances; while the availability of isotopes has made it possible to follow the movements of single types of atom from substance to substance, and from place to place, within the cell. Although living creatures are deplorably complicated, they seem to work by means of a relatively small number of basic tricks: for example, energy transport within the cell appears to be carried on by exchanging a single currency, adenosine triphosphate. This substance powers a wide variety of processes: when it is added to extracts of a firefly's tail, the mixture glows with light; when it is added to proteins extracted from muscle, the proteins contract. Again, control of growth and development appears to be exercised through another small group of substances, the nucleic acids. These seem to be capable of bearing coded instructions and of duplicating them, thus providing the alphabet for heredity.

Knowledge of the structures within the cell has expanded rapidly with the development of electron microscopy. Previously, using light microscopy, details smaller than about 5,000 Ångstroms ($1\text{Å} = 10^{-8}$ cm) could not be resolved, so there was no way of knowing what small but important structures were hidden from view. Now there is nowhere for structures to hide; the electron microscope (resolution 10—15)Å can reveal them even if they are only a few water molecules wide, and it appears that living structures have an orderly arrangement right down to their molecular components, like gigantic and complex crystals. One disadvantage of the electron microscope is that it can be used only on dried, dead tissue; so that other studies are required in order to correlate ultrastructure with function. Such a combined attack has already yielded results that have greatly advanced our understanding of muscular contraction.

The development of exceedingly fine glass micro-electrodes, that can be inserted into single living cells without damaging them, has vastly increased our knowledge of excitability and of the conduction of nervous impulses. These processes all seem to depend on the distribution of various inorganic ions inside and outside the cells, in conjunction with the selective, and controllable, permeability of the cell membrane. In this type of investigation, and in many others, electronic techniques have been applied on a large scale. The appearance of most physiological laboratories has changed completely since the days of the induction coil. They are now filled with racks of electronics equipment, and the tissue being investigated may be hard to find.

Most of the organs in the body can work only when many different types of cell cooperate, and much physiological research is concerned with this higher level of functional organization. One recent advance has been in our knowledge of kidney function, as a result of the application of ideas derived from chemical engineering. There have also been strikingly successful applications of basic physiological knowledge to the solution of practical problems; for example, in combating the effects of high altitudes or in designing machines to take over the functions of heart and lungs during surgical operations.

The research problem posed by the highly integrated functions is formidable. Making experiments on the nervous system, for instance, is like trying to investigate a huge computer that works on unknown principles: to make matters still more difficult, the whole thing is submerged in seawater, and the most delicate tool available is an electrical probe the size of a crowbar! Understandably, therefore, physiologists are perplexed about the best strategy to follow. Should they first try to elucidate the properties of the individual units and of their extremely complex connexions? Or may it be possible to infer the nature of the mechanism from observations on large pieces of it, perhaps using concepts derived from the study of man-made computers?

Thus, although we are beginning to comprehend something about the origin of life, we are still far from understanding the objective basis of intelligence or of human nature. The history of science teaches patience, and in the meantime we must make about these important subjects that most characteristically scientific of statements: " We don't know yet ".

XIV—Future Field of Zoology

By C. F. A. Pantin, F.R.S.
Professor of Zoology, University of Cambridge

TWO generations ago zoology was well defined. Its prime object was to trace the ancestry of animals through comparative anatomy. " Living fossils " like the coelacanth fish, or that strange mollusc *Neopilina*, surviving 400 million years after the rest of its kind, still excite interest. But today zoology is the most varied of the sciences. It includes the identification of species, their evolution, genetics, behaviour, ecology, natural conservation and control; and the comparative physiology and biochemistry of animals, the structure and machinery of their cells, the interaction of their living tissues and the development of the organism.

All these present different problems, in pure science, agriculture, fisheries and medicine. Much is required of the men who investigate them. A museum taxonomist today must know many more species than did his grandfather—those of insects alone are now estimated at about a million. He must also be a statistician. He must know more of other sciences. Genetics has changed his notion of species; and specific characters even include the chemical differences of serology.

But the characteristic of zoology today is interest in living machinery. The manner

A " living fossil "—the coelacanth caught off the coast of South Africa.

in which a fish swims is an engineering problem. The organization of the nervous system has parallels with electronic circuits. Because of their practical importance in the natural world, insects have received special attention. Particularly through British biologists, their physiology is now known almost as well as our own. There are no more instructive experiments than those showing how growth, moulting and metamorphosis in insects are controlled by the action of a succession of hormones. There is a ruthless simplicity about insect physiology. They harden their cuticle by tanning. They make it waterproof by secreting wax dissolved in petrol. Some withstand very low temperatures by loading the blood with glycerol—a strange parallel to antifreeze.

The sense organs of insects include instructive engineering devices. In the two-winged flies, the hind wings are reduced to a pair of oscillating dumb-bells that are used by the animal to control position after the fashion of a gyro-compass. But the most remarkable thing about insects is the complexity of their behaviour. The classical work of von Frisch on honey-bees showed their astonishing power to learn, and to communicate with others, and to use sensory information that is not available to ourselves—as in the use of polarized light for navigation.

Many of the features of behaviour in insects and other animals can be imitated in significant ways by electronic sensory and computing devices. But the most remarkable feature of all was perceived by Darwin:

> . . . the wonderfully diversified instincts, mental powers, and affections of ants are notorious, yet their cerebral ganglia are not so large as the quarter of a small pin's head . . . the brain of an ant is one of the most marvellous atoms of matter in the world, perhaps more so than the brain of man.

It has been said that nature provides an animal suitable for the study of every kind of biological problem. How eggs are fertilized, how embryos develop, how wounds heal, how nerves regenerate after damage, are easily studied in invertebrates, newts and chicks. With the electron microscope the zoologist can study structure even down to molecular dimensions: and the " protoplasm " of cells is found to be far more highly organized than the homogeneous slime described in old text-books.

But the greatest tasks that face the zoologist concern animals and man in nature; the control of food supplies, insect pests, or disease. Production of an insecticide is easy. Prediction of the result of its indiscriminate use is exceedingly difficult. We try to control nature, and by a curious paradox we change the natural world more rapidly and unpredictably than ever before. Here are the most difficult problems that face our own future.

An electron-micrograph of the locomotor " flagella " of the Protozoan Trichonympha, magnified 45,000 times. From a paper by I. R. Gibbons and A. V. Grinstone in *The Journal of Biophysical and Biochemical Cytology*.

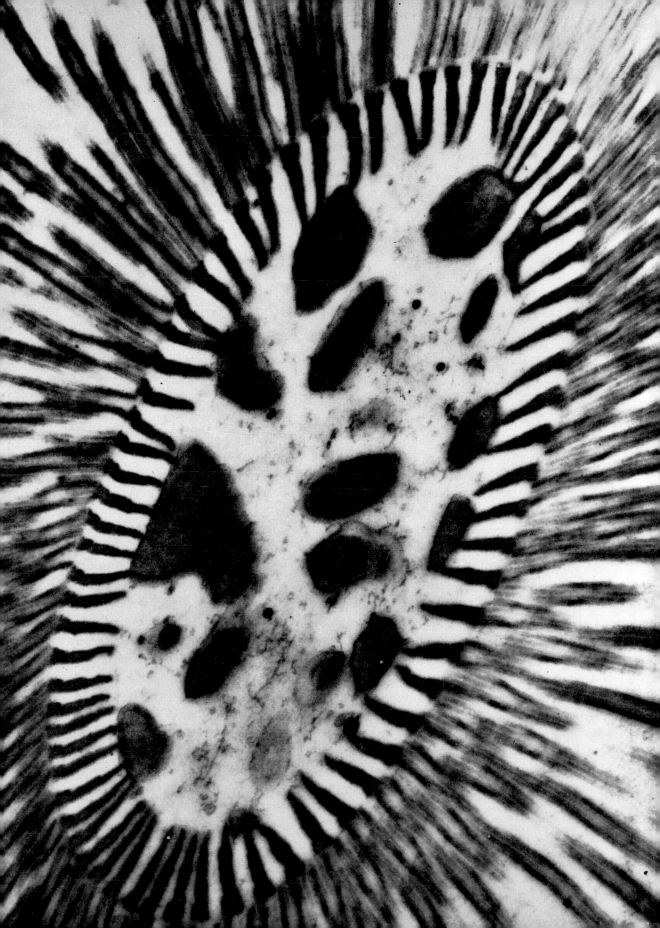

IMPARTIAL BULWARK THROUGH THREE CENTURIES

By D. C. Martin, C.B.E.

Assistant Secretary of the Royal Society

ALTHOUGH the Royal Society is a private and independent body dedicated to the promotion of natural knowledge, upon the present fellows falls an inheritance of labour ungrudgingly given for the public service during three centuries. Unlike many other national academies, the Society receives no state funds for its own private purposes as a learned society, and thus it can give advice which has the weight and finality of a disinterested opinion.

The Society has steadily advanced in public esteem and become a kind of council to which various departments in the Government can and do appeal for advice and assistance in matters where expert scientific knowledge is needed. Today there are many specialized societies and many government organizations each devoted to the cultivation of special branches of research, but the Royal Society remains at the head as the one great national corporation in the country that embraces in its purview the whole wide realm of nature and elects into its fellowship the most worthy representatives of every department of natural science in the British Commonwealth. It is not surprising that such a body has many calls on it.

In the Society's earliest days there were many contacts with its royal founder, and in 1662 it was the King's pleasure " that no patent should pass for any philosophical or mechanical invention until examined by the Society ". The national position of the Society was thus very early established by King Charles II. Queen Anne in 1710 placed the Royal Greenwich Observatory in the sole charge of the Society. Its President is still Chairman of the Board of Visitors. In connexion with the observatory, the Society took a share in the alteration of the calendar, known as the Change of Style, which took place in 1752. The Bill was drawn up by Peter Davall, a

134

secretary of the Society. There was much popular discontent at the change, and the illness and death of Bradley, then the Astronomer Royal, which took place shortly after the change, was attributed to a judgment from heaven.

In about 1750 the Lord Mayor of London, two of the judges, and an alderman died within a year from gaol fever caught at the Old Bailey sessions, and the Society's help was solicited. A committee was set up to investigate ventilation in gaols. A ventilator, invented by a member of the committee, was set up in Newgate and the number of deaths dropped from eight a week to two a month. It was about this time, too, that the Society was asked to consider the best form of protection of buildings from lightning. Benjamin Franklin, a greatly respected scientist, advocated sharp-pointed lightning conductors and others round-ended ones. As Franklin was an American colonist, there were political opponents to his views, and it is said that the King invited the president to find in favour of the rounded lightning conductor, to which the president had to reply that the laws of nature do not change even for a king. King George III does not seem to have taken offence, for he gave the Society strong support for many different scientific enterprises, for example, to a geodetical survey with a view to connecting the trigonometrical surveys between the observatories at Greenwich and Paris.

This, too, was the period when the Society memorialized the Government for support of many scientific expeditions through grants of money or use of ships. These included two expeditions in 1761 and 1769 to observe the transit of Venus, the voyages of Captain Cook and, somewhat later, the search for the North-West Passage and other polar explorations. After Cook's expedition, which set sail in 1772 and circumnavigated the globe, the Society awarded him its Copley Medal for the means he had taken to preserve the health of his crew.

Towards the end of the last century the Society and its fellows undertook the great work of preparing a catalogue of scientific papers that had appeared in all parts of the world since 1800. This involved over 40 years' unstinted labour by fellows, which put all men of science in their debt. Such was the increase of scientific papers that when it was suggested to continue into the twentieth century it was proposed that it be done on an international basis. A brave start was made, but the Society carried the heavy end of the cost and responsibility for the International Catalogue of Scientific Literature completed up to the end of 1915. In 1935, when the project was finally wound up, the Society had expended over £14,000 that it had no means of recovering. This took no account of the great labour freely rendered by its fellows in this great public-spirited enterprise.

At the end of the nineteenth century the Society along with others, particularly the

British Association for the Advancement of Science, urged the creation of a national laboratory. A Treasury committee, of which Lord Rayleigh was chairman, recommended that a public institution should be founded for standardizing and verifying instruments, for testing materials and for the determination of physical constants. It also recommended that it be placed under the control of the Royal Society. This was done under an agreed scheme of organization whereby the President and Council appoint a general board representative of all the principal national interests, and also an executive committee. The work of the new National Physical Laboratory, as it was named, began under its first director, Dr. R. T. Glazebrook, F.R.S., at Kew Observatory, and in December, 1900, Queen Victoria made a grant of Bushy House and its 23 acres of ground, a royal residence at Teddington, for the uses of the laboratory. The laboratory at Bushy House was formally opened by the Prince and Princess of Wales on March 19, 1902. The scientific programme of the laboratory, which has grown from strength to strength, is still governed by its general board and executive committee appointed by the President and Council of the Royal Society although its financial administration has been in the care of the Department of Scientific and Industrial Research since 1918.

Since 1900 the Government have continued their practice of referring various scientific matters to the council for investigation and report. In 1902 the Colonial Office asked for volcanic phenomena in the West Indies to be the subject of a report; in 1936 seismic activity in the island of Montserrat was investigated, and the Society continues its interest in this subject in the West Indies. Tropical diseases have also been investigated on behalf of the Colonial Office: malaria in 1903, Malta fever in 1907, cattle disease in Central and South Africa at various times between 1910 and 1930, kala-azar in North China in 1925-27, and in the Mediterranean in 1930, filaria and nephritis in British Guiana in 1927-29; and work on leprosy in West Africa is now being done by one of the Society's research fellows.

Just before the Second World War the Society took the initiative in compiling a register of scientific and technical personnel in the country. This proved invaluable in the diposition of the country's scientific resources, and was later taken over by the Ministry of Labour and National Service. During the war the president and secretaries were members of the Scientific Advisory Committee of the War Cabinet.

Soon after the war was ended the Society, with the support of the Government, organized the Royal Society Empire Scientific Conference, which was opened by King George VI in June, 1946, and attended by scientists from the whole Commonwealth. Before this, fellows of the Society had, in fact, prepared a blue-print of the postwar needs of scientific research in this country, and this did much for a speedy return to civil scientific research in British universities. As a result of one of the many recommendations of the Empire Scientific Conference, the Society in 1948 held the Royal Society Scientific Information Conference. These two conferences are splendid examples of how, through the Society, the Governments of Commonwealth countries can receive advice and assistance from the scientific community on scientific matters of basic concern to national developments.

A valuable cooperative Commonwealth scheme created by the Society in 1953 is the Commonwealth Bursaries Scheme supported by annual grants from all the Commonwealth countries and the Nuffield Foundation. This enables scientists of proven merit to study within the Commonwealth with persons or at places specially suitable for the further development of their respective researches.

The Society's role in international scientific relations is described elsewhere but the unique role of the Society in formulating and coordinating a British national research programme was well exemplified in the International Geophysical Year (I.G.Y.). The Society with the active participation of all concerned—the Meteorological Office, the Radio Research Station of the D.S.I.R. and many universities—prepared a coordinated programme of the United Kingdom contribution and discussed it with the Treasury. The funds for the university work were provided through the Royal Society by a special parliamentary grant-in-aid for the I.G.Y., and the additional costs falling on the Government research stations were provided and accounted for through the usual departmental channels. This proved to be a highly successful pattern of cooperation.

The grant-in-aid also covered the cost of the Royal Society's I.G.Y. Antarctic Expeditions 1956-58, which so notably maintained the Society's tradition of scientific expeditions. One outcome of the I.G.Y. has been the new developments in space research. The well proved parliamentary grant-in-aid method of supporting the university programme is, however, not being adopted. Nevertheless, the Society, through its British National Committee for Space Research, does, in fact, coordinate the British projects concerned with the tracking and instrumentation of satellites and the rocket experiments. It also provides the scientific advice for the programme as a whole and conducts its associated international scientific relations.

The parliamentary grant-in-aid method, which has been shown to be so well suited for the Government support of research through the Royal Society, began as a result of a request first made to the Society in 1849, when the Government asked the help of the Society to apply a grant " for the promotion of scientific inquiries ". The first grant was £1,000. This practice has continued, and today the grant is

£75,000. This is most carefully administered by eight boards meeting three times a year and making recommendations to the Society's council. The boards give expert and most careful scrutiny to applications received. Last year 80 grants were given, about 20 of them for expeditions. This willing and expert service of fellows is typical of the important role the Society can play in encouraging scientific advances to the national advantage. More use could be made of it. Parliamentary grants-in-aid are also administered by the Society for scientific publications and for international relations, the respective amounts this year being £10,000 and £42,500.

By Acts of Parliament, the President of the Royal Society is consulted about all new appointments to the Agricultural Research Council, the Medical Research Council, the Research Council of the D.S.I.R. and several other important government research bodies. It is now common practice to seek his advice about many other scientific appointments. The council nominates representatives to many other public organizations. At present about 100 of the fellows serve in this capacity on some 70 different governing bodies, including the University Courts of Bristol, Exeter, Hull, and Liverpool, as well as other university bodies, and as governors of Charterhouse, Christ's Hospital, Dulwich, Eton, Harrow, King's School, Grantham, Rugby, Shrewsbury, Westminster and Winchester. Among other appointments the President is, ex officio, a trustee of the British Museum, an honorary member of the Royal Irish Academy, a governor of the City and Guilds of London Institute, a member of the *Spectator* committee and *The Times* Holding Company. The Society is among the very limited number of public bodies to which is conceded by prescription or otherwise the privilege of presenting loyal addresses whenever it is appropriate to do so to the Sovereign on the Throne.

In its 300th year the Society's patronage is more widely sought than ever before. Its reputation has been built up by its determination from the beginning to keep the highest attainable standards in seeking to improve natural knowledge. Its support is only given when there is no conflict with its chartered purpose and when there is likely to be no departure from its own high standards. Maintaining its high example is by itself perhaps the greatest public responsibility of all.

SCIENCE AND INDUSTRY

I—Nuclear Power Economic by 1970?

By Sir Christopher Hinton, K.B.E., F.R.S.

TO think, as many people do, that the development of nuclear power called only for the design of successful reactors is quite wrong. In the years between 1946 and 1956 it was not Calder Hall but a new industry that was built; the reactors could not work without the supporting plants at Springfields, where uranium is extracted from the ore, purified, converted into metal, and made into fuel elements, at Capenhurst, where the uranium is enriched, and at Windscale, where the irradiated fuel elements are chemically treated to remove the fission products and plutonium. Each of these ancillary plants was more complex than the reactors; in these first 10 years only a third of our design and development teams worked on reactors, two-thirds were on the ancillary plants.

That these plants were designed, built, and put into operation quickly and successfully was due to the fact that scientists and engineers worked together in closely knit teams, the scientists knowing the difficulties of the engineers and the engineers understanding the limitations of the scientists. Many techniques that can be useful in conventional industry were developed in these years; the organization for integrating research and design to achieve quick industrial results could be one of the most important.

But these great pioneering days, when the ancillary plants of the atomic energy industry presented so many problems, are now over. Their further development is, today, conventional and it is in the development of nuclear reactors that the greatest developments must come.

In every prime mover the cost of generating power has fallen as with the passage of time, it becomes possible to achieve higher temperatures in the heat cycle. Watt's engine using a top temperature of 212°F. used 8lb. of coal an hour for each horse-power developed; modern power plants using top temperatures of 1,050°F. use only 0.8lb. of coal per hour per horse-power, and there are similar economies in capital cost. The energy of fission in a nuclear reactor is released at a very high temperature, but metallurgical and other considerations limit the temperatures at which the heat can be recovered and used. In the Windscale reactors, built against a tight time schedule for producing military plutonium, the temperature of recovery was so low that power could not be generated from the heat. Research lifted these temperature limitations, and at Calder Hall the heat was recovered at a temperature just high enough to make power generation possible.

The main stream of nuclear reactor research must flow in the direction of higher temperatures. The present limitations are in the fuel element, which in reactors of the Calder Hall type is a bar of metallic uranium enclosed in a magnesium alloy can. Neither metal can be used at temperatures appreciably higher than at present, because uranium undergoes an allotropic transformation at 660°C. and the can has an upper working temperature of about 450°C. Beryllium and stainless steel are alternative canning materials, and extensive research is being done on them; the problems associated with metallic uranium can be avoided by using it in ceramic form and it is proposed to use uranium oxide to make higher temperatures possible.

To give operating experience of these developments the Atomic Energy Authority is building the Advanced Gas-Cooled Reactor at Windscale; it is the logical step forward, but as still higher temperatures are sought we shall reach new limitations. Possibly the most important will be those connected with the use of graphite as moderator, and it may be necessary to evade these difficulties by using a replaceable graphite moderator (as is proposed in the high temperature gas-cooled reactor now in its early development stages at Winfrith Heath) or perhaps by using heavy water as the moderator.

Meanwhile work by A.E.A. on the Fast Breeder Reactor continues at Dounreay, aimed to develop a system in which the by-product plutonium from thermal reactors of the Calder Hall or A.G.R. type can be used as the fuel. It presents problems of great difficulty and it is doubtful whether it can be in industrial use within the next 10 years.

Nuclear power from the industrial plants at present being built will be more expensive than from conventional plants built concurrently. This is contrary to what was expected when the original industrial programme was approved in 1955; the changed position is due partly to a reduction in the credit given for the by-product plutonium, partly to the rise in interest rates and partly to the spectacular technical advances in conventional power plants. Nor is there the shortage of coal which was

Building the advanced gas-cooled reactor at Windscale, Cumberland.

thought, in 1957, to make a large nuclear programme immediately necessary. But demand for electrical power doubles every 10 years, and if coal were the only fuel used for generation the industry would require about 115m. tons a year by 1975. With total coal production around 200m. tons a year it is obvious that other fuels must be necessary to meet national requirements by the mid-1970s. The history of develop-

ment of nuclear power and the present promise of research lead one to believe that for base load generation nuclear power will be cheaper than conventional power by 1970. This cannot be achieved without a sufficiently large industrial programme; research is ineffective if it runs too far ahead of practical application and the test of use. It is the need and promise of the future that justify the present programme.

Two reactors under construction at the nuclear power station, Bradwell, Essex.

II—Following Faraday's Lead

By Sir Willis Jackson, F.R.S.

THE subject of electrical engineering had its origins in science, and its progress has been continually stimulated and frequently revitalized by scientific discovery, notably by new discoveries in physics. This progress has in turn provided new electrical tools for further scientific investigation, and the continuous interplay between the two has been of profound benefit to both.

Parsons 75 kW. turbines at Forth Banks Power Station, 1892.

Its history may be said to have begun with the publication in 1600 by William Gilbert, of Colchester, of his famous book *De Magnete* on magnetism and electricity, followed in 1675 by the first book devoted entirely to electricity by Robert Boyle, one of the original fellows of the Royal Society and a member of its first council. These beginnings were extended and clarified by physicists such as Volta (1745-1827), Ampere (1775-1836), Oersted (1777-1851), and Ohm (1787-1854), all elected to foreign membership of the Royal Society, whose names now serve to describe important units in the subject.

To Michael Faraday (1791-1867) goes the great distinction, through his discovery of the principle of electro-magnetic induction, of initiating the many practical applications of electricity. This discovery was published in a paper read before the Royal Society on November 24, 1831. Thereafter he turned his attention mainly to research in other directions, being characteristically uninterested in anything suggestive of commercialism, and left to his contemporaries the exploitation of this promising new principle.

Inventors were not lacking, and from 1832 there was a steady stream of proposals for electromagnetic machines of various designs. Even so, the development of the electrical generator did not begin to take industrial form until the 1870s, and was preceded in this respect by that of land and submarine telegraphy under the stimulation in this country of Charles Wheatstone (1802-1875) and Lord Kelvin (1824-1907).

A few important landmarks were the invention of the telephone by Alexander Graham Bell (1847-1922) in 1876; the opening of the first electric power station in London for supplying street lighting installations in 1882; Sebastion Z. de Ferranti's (1964-1930) courageous development in the late 1890s of electrical power transmission from a station at Deptford by underground cable at 10,000 volts; the invention of wireless telegraphy by Guglielmo Marconi (1874-1919) towards the end of the century; the pioneer work in the same period of J. J. Thomson (1856-1940) on the flow of electricity through high vacua, and his experimental discovery of the electron; the invention of the thermionic diode by J. A. Fleming (1849-1945) in 1904 and of the triode by Lee de Forest (b. 1873) two years later; and the supporting theoretical work of men such as Maxwell (1831-1879), Heaviside (1850-1925), and Hertz (1857-1894).

Based on these and many subsequent scientific discoveries and technical inventions electrical engineering has grow rapidly during the past 50 years until the value of the products of the electrical industry of this country in 1959 totalled some £1,400m. The pace of development during the past 20 years can only be described as fantastic, for during this period there have evolved such achievements as

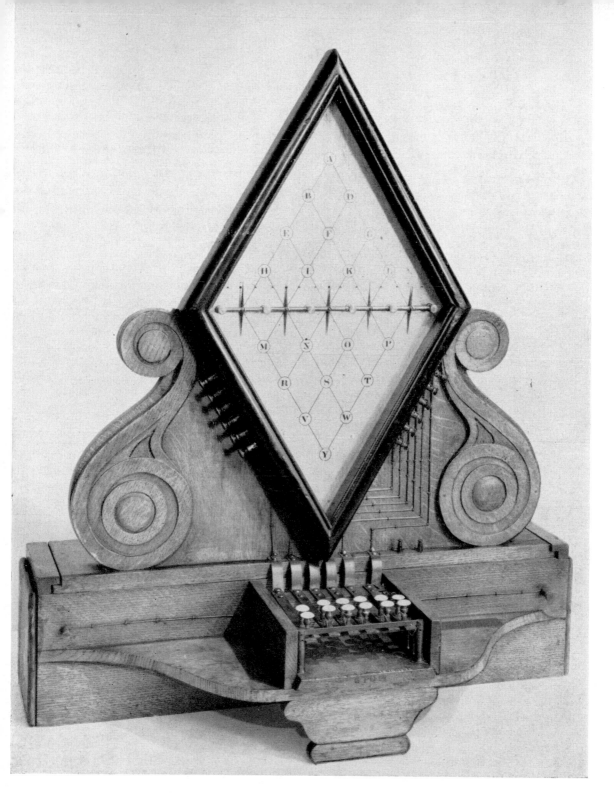

Cooke and Wheatstone's five-needle telegraph, invented in 1837.

television and radar, systems of micro-wave, and of transatlantic submarine telephonic communication; electrical digital computers; closed-loop servo-mechanisms and other forms of automatic control; new scientific instruments such as the electron microscope and the mass spectrometer; a whole range of high-energy particle accelerators; the nuclear power reactor; and the prospect of power generation through controlled thermo-nuclear reactions.

Perhaps not so spectacular, and certainly not so widely publicized, progress in respect of previously well-established forms of electrical equipment has been no less meritorious and significant: such as, during the past decade, the improvement in the thermal efficiency of steam turbine driven electrical generators from 29 to 34 per cent, the decrease in the weight per unit rating of these sets by about 35 per cent, the increase in power rating of large transformers by a factor of 5 and of high-voltage switchgear by 20 or more.

Of vital importance to this progress has been the increasing participation of chemists, physicists, metallurgists and mathematicians in the activities of the electrical industry, with respect particularly to the production of new magnetic, insulating, semi-conducting and structural materials. The emergence of the transistor within less than 10 years from the scientific study of highly purified germanium to an economic replacement for the thermionic valve in many applications and the achievement of a 60 megawatt nuclear power station within 17 years of the first artificial disintegration of the nucleus of uranium are outstanding examples of the intimate collaboration between scientists and professional engineers that is characteristic of the electrical industry. The prospects of further progress are likely to be bound up increasingly with the cooperative exploration and exploitation of the regions that lie between the traditional scientific and technological disciplines, and the Royal Society is in a unique position in this country to stimulate this pursuit.

III—Harnessing Nature's Power

By A. J. S. Pippard, M.B.E., F.R.S.
Emeritus Professor of Civil Engineering, University of London

THE charter definition of civil engineering as " the art of directing the great sources of power in nature for the use and convenience of man " presupposes a working knowledge of science, but even before the Royal Charter was granted to the 10-year-old Institution of Civil Engineers in 1828, the founders of that institution had specified one of its objects to be the promotion of natural philosophy. It is therefore not surprising that a test of proficiency in scientific subjects is imposed as an essential requirement for entry to the profession.

For a long time qualification was normally achieved by passing the examinations of the institution during, or after, pupilage under a corporate member, but with the introduction of engineering studies into the universities, steadily increasing numbers chose to undergo the discipline of such courses, and today about 80 per cent of those who qualify for professional status possess either a university degree or a diploma of similar standard awarded by a college of technology.

This scientific education is based largely on pure and applied mathematics, but these alone, in their classical forms, are inadequate to meet the requirements of engineering design; consequently portions of the theory of elasticity, hydro-dynamics and other branches of applied mechanics have been adapted to the special needs of the engineer and the subjects of strength of materials, theory of structures and hydraulics have evolved. These subjects, with geology, soil mechanics, surveying and some thermodynamics and principles of electricity, form the basis of academic civil engineering studies. The efficiency of this education must be judged by the extent to which it enables the civil engineer to keep abreast of scientific thought, by its ability to stimulate research and, most important, on how it is translated into works of construction.

The necessity for a lively interest in science if the profession is to flourish was appreciated by Tredgold, when, in the

147

Completed after four years' work: the Kariba Dam.

definition of civil engineering mentioned earlier, he said: " Its bounds are unlimited and equally so must be the researches of its professors ".

The early professors, i.e., practitioners, had to rely for scientific guidance largely on men who were not themselves engineers, and much is owed to mathematicians and physicists for their contributions to the embryo science.

The engineer must remain dependent on the pure scientist for fundamental discoveries, but once these have been estab-

lished their practical exploitation is his concern, and the necessity for research should be immediately apparent. It is only comparatively recently that its importance has been adequately appreciated; for too long, engineering research was neglected not only by the practitioner but even by most of the universities. Today, however, no university department would be content unless it could claim some direct interest in research, and this new attitude is spreading rapidly to other than academic circles. Many engineers now

When the M1 was built.   A Euclid loader discharging into a bottom-dump truck.

Below: Members of the Road Research Laboratory measure the bearing power of soil under a road bed.

appreciate the possibility and desirability of carrying out investigations in the course of their normal practice in order to provide data for the future.

Structures such as Kariba and Dokan dams, the new bridges over the Forth and Severn, the demands for more economical use of steel in large building frames, the enormous possibilities in the use of prestressed concrete and thin shells, all emphasize the problems of construction; and when the equally important fields of hydraulic engineering in its many aspects, public health, highways and others are added, we may well agree with Tredgold that the bounds are unlimited and hope that the correct moral with regard to research will be drawn.

The Building Research Station, the Road Research Laboratory, the Hydraulics Research Laboratory and the Water Pollution Research Laboratory give invaluable service to the civil engineer; and while university research is necessarily more individual and less dependent on team work than that of the official establishments, the two should be complementary. Apart from the intrinsic value of the work of university laboratories, which is considerable, their healthy development is a matter of national concern, since it is on them that the Government departments must rely to recruit research staff for their own work.

Engineering research is expensive, and it is not easy for the universities to obtain adequate funds to develop their potentialities properly. The Institution of Civil Engineers, recognizing this and in fulfilment of their charter obligations, have recently inaugurated a Civil Engineering Research Fund with the financial support of a number of contractors and consulting engineers. This will demonstrate not only the faith of the profession as a whole in the vital importance of research but also its determination to show by its own efforts that it is worthy of such help from Government funds as will enable British civil engineers to maintain and increase the prestige they now enjoy throughout the world.

IV—Old Techniques Yield to New

By O. A. Saunders, F.R.S.

Professor of Mechanical Engineering, Imperial College, University of London

MODERN industry was founded on mechanical science and is still dependent on it. Other branches such as electrical, chemical and metallurgical sciences are now also responsible for great new industries, but in all these activities mechanical science is involved in the design and construction of all industrial plant.

Science today contributes to the progress of the engineering industry in three broad

An engraving in the Science Museum by H. Beighton of the Newcomen engine, designed in 1717 for raising water.

ways: first, by the discovery of new principles, through the application of which the engineer may achieve his aims; secondly, by helping to provide new materials and production processes; and lastly, by indicating how to improve the general and detailed design of all kinds of engineering appliances.

This century has seen many spectacular examples of great industries founded on new scientific principles, as for example in radio and electronics, aircraft and aero engines, artificial fibres. The availability of new materials has also had widespread effects, examples being stainless and corrosion resisting steels, high temperature steels, ceramics and plastics. The influence of the third kind of scientific activity on engineering progress, although perhaps less spectacular, is equally important, since it is often the performance of component machinery that decides whether or not a new development will be successful, and the prospects of its rapid commercial exploitation usually depend on finding satisfactory and economic methods of construction.

This is especially true of the mechanical engineering industry, which provides machinery and plant for almost every branch of industry and therefore occupies a key position in the application of science to industry today. This is not to say that mechanical engineering exists only to serve other branches; there are many familiar examples of outstanding scientific develop-

ments in mechanical engineering itself. Power generation by steam turbine or internal combustion engine has reached advanced stages of development aided by science, particularly in the nuclear power station projects and in the gas turbine for aircraft propulsion.

In the immediate future there are many directions in which the further application of science may lead to a rapid advance in mechanical engineering. To mention only a few: the much more extensive use of metal-forming processes, such as the extrusion of metals, to replace the comparatively wasteful metal cutting process in the production of a wide range of parts in industries such as the motor industry, where the cost of materials is high, may prove very profitable; the production under high pressures of new materials with special properties may have great value; the wider use of hydraulic transmission systems, with their inherent advantages over electric transmission, offers promise in power transmission in vehicles and machinery. In all these, and many other cases, progress depends on scientific research.

The need for conserving our national resources both in power and in materials offers a challenge to the scientist to devise less wasteful methods of utilizing existing material resources. In the power production field the eventual elimination of the restriction of the thermodynamic cycle, although not an immediate prospect, would have far reaching effects.

In all new developments and also in many comparatively unexplored areas of existing conventional plant and processes, there is great scope in mechanical engineering for applying fundamental scientific principles to improve design. Many of the great engineers of the past established reputations as inspired designers, and engineering design today remains the heart of the engineer's work, still calling for much of the element of art; but the part played by science rapidly increases as research leads to more knowledge of engineering processes. In a competitive world progress becomes harder, and the engineering industry looks to the scientist for new ideas and new methods to replace many older rule of thumb techniques.

If industry is to reap the full benefits of science, the resources of scientific manpower must be distributed to the best advantage between universities, research organizations, and industry itself. It is not easy to tell whether the present distribution is the most effective. Until recently the bulk of fundamental research was done at the universities, but other groups have now entered this field. It is important that enough scientific effort be put on the study of the actual processes of industry, and that scientists in all three kinds of employment have as many contacts and opportunities for working together as possible.

V—Materials Problem of Supersonic Flight

By Major P. L. Teed, O.B.E.

EXERCISING his greatest asset, imagination, man had even before the time of the mythical Daedelus and his unlucky son, Icarus, aspired to emulate the flight of birds. If one neglects, on the grounds of lack of space and of uncertainty of facts, the concepts of Leonardo da Vinci, it was not until the earlier part of the nineteenth century that the fundamental principles of flight were really appreciated with the achievements of Sir George Cayley, a Yorkshire squire.

Birds have both weight and wings, and the ratio of these varies from about $\frac{1}{4}$lb. a sq. ft. of wing area in the case of Leach's Petrel, to many times this amount with some less skilled performers. With guidance of this type, the squire was able to make a glider and to make his unwilling coachman (whose name is unfortunately unknown) the first aviator. Cayley had appreciated the importance of the inter-relationship of weight and of supporting surface, but, unlike his flapping, soaring

mentors, he was without means of creating propulsive thrust. For this, the light power plant (mainly the invention of Gottlieb Daimler) was adapted early in this century for aeronautical purposes by those inspired bicycle makers, the Wright brothers. Since their Kittyhawk flights of December, 1903, aviation has depended for its development on increasing knowledge of the medium in which we fly and of the properties of the materials used to do so.

The Wrights' historical craft was somewhat spitefully described by one of their contemporary compatriots as " a stick and string box kite with a gasoline buggy engine ". It was nevertheless a very wonderful thing. Its airframe was mostly of wood, wire-braced and fabric covered. Its power plant was an uncertain engine of only 12 h.p. The bulk of the machine was made of non-metallic materials, but as the size and speed of aircraft increased these were largely eliminated for sound engineering reasons, but, as will be seen

154

later, some still remain and provide one of the many anxieties of those having to deal with the problems of sustained high supersonic flight. Today, in an era of high *sub*sonic speeds, about three-quarters of the airframe is made of wrought heat-treated aluminium alloy, but, if sustained high *super*sonic speeds are to be the order of the day, such materials will no longer be suitable. They can nevertheless provide the entrée to the supersonic age.

As is generally known, with increase in height above sea level, the temperature of the air progressively decreases. This is, however, too abbreviated a statement. In the troposphere, in which we have our normal being, the statement is indeed true, but in the stratosphere, in which, for technical reasons, the bulk of supersonic flight will be carried out, increase in altitude produces no decrease in temperature. In this region, regardless of height up to 100,000ft., it is taken as a result of international agreement as being — 56.5°C or — 69.70°F. Were the wrought aluminium alloys of the airframe to attain the stratospheric temperature, this would not be a disadvantage, for the mechanical properties of such alloys improve with decrease in temperature. When the flight speed is supersonic, however, those parts of the airframe in contact with the stratospheric atmosphere do not decrease in temperature but undergo kinetic heating because of gaseous friction.

Soundly based figures of the Royal Aircraft Establishment give the relationship in the stratosphere between speed and temperature: at the velocity of sound above the tropopause, say at 660 miles an hour, the ultimate temperature of exposed parts of the airframe, not influenced either by insulation or by refrigeration, will be 0°C or 32°F. At twice the sonic velocity at this height it will be 80°C or 176°F, while at three times it will be 200°C or 392°F. The mechanical properties of metallic materials change with their temperature: while generally with decrease in temperature the static strength of most alloys is improved or unaltered, on the other hand, with increase in temperature it is decreased. Only within certain limits are these changes reversible. Heat-treatable aluminium alloys, unprotected by insulation or refrigeration, will be permanently weakened by sustained stratospheric flight exceeding about 1,500 miles an hour. With a number of titanium alloys and steels, however, a decrease in mechanical strength at this speed will be trifling, and on returning to normal ground level temperatures the original properties will be completely restored. This enables one to say that aluminium alloys will continue to be employed as the main structural material up to about the speed already mentioned. In excess of this, titanium alloys may be advantageously used, but should speeds of 2,500 to 3,000 miles an hour be the target, then steel, probably the heat treatable austenitic varieties, will take their place.

155

Supersonic tests are made on model aircraft in this wind tunnel at the Royal Aircraft Establishment, Bedford, designed to test aircraft of the future.

Unfortunately this is by no means the complete story, the implications of which involve research and yet more research. In the aeroplane of today, certain organic materials are regarded as essentials. They are used for transparencies, tyres, radomes, fuel tanks, joint seals (for the pressurized portion of the craft, &c.), and as fuel. Omitting the last, it is impossible to say without considerable investigation, doubtless involving invention, what satisfactory substitutes can be employed in machines having sustained speeds of more than 1,700 to 1,800 miles an hour. The problems are not thought to be insoluble but they may constitute a temporary check in further development. Finality in aircraft performance is not yet in sight, nor is it likely to be brought about by the inadequacy of available materials.

156

VI—Imaginative Chemists

By Sir Alexander Fleck, K.B.E., F.R.S.

THE chemical industry is second to none in acknowledging what the Royal Society has done over the 300 years of its existence to make possible those technological advances that have now given us sophisticated chemistry woven into the structure of the modern chemical business. That means that many sciences and many disciplines have been brought to bear on the industrial development to carry it up to its present standards.

The Royal Society has always been catholic in its approaches to the various sciences, and the chemical industry has gained as much as any other industry from this basic method, particularly in this century.

The classification of the chemical industry into its various sections is influenced more than in most industries by definition. However, we shall not be led far astray if we think of it in nine fields: (a) Alkali; (b) Electro chemical; (c) Acids and general inorganic chemicals; (d) Fertilizers; (e) Heavy organic chemicals and petro-chemicals; (f) Plastics; (g) Man-made fibres; (h) Dyes; (i) Pharmaceuticals. It is thus seen that the industry is by no means a simple one, but one that demands the skilled use of many varying techniques. Further, the economic philosophy may be quite different in one field to that wisely applied in another: the research and development organizations for, say, pharmaceuticals may well have little similarity to those used for, say, electro-chemical products: the capital cost per ton year for, say, alkali is widely different from the products of the dyes industry. Thus the economics of the industry are by no means easy to define, and are certainly not uniform as between one product and another.

Within the past three or four decades, the dominant characteristics of the human side of the industry have markedly changed. In the 1900s the predominant type of process (of which there were exceptions) required hard manual work, frequently had to contend with hot furnace-like conditions, and often had to put up with dirty, dusty atmospheres that sent a man home from his day's work obviously labelled a

157

hardy son of toil, far indeed from being a white-collared worker. Additionally, it would then not have been regarded as very exceptional if he were asked to labour up to 84 hours a week, including a 24-hour change-over shift. Apart from the long hours, one basic reason for the unattractive conditions was that the then chemical industry was mainly concerned with handling in its processes solid material: liquids and gases played a minor part. Today, that balance has swung very much the other way and liquids and gases, thoroughly studied in the light of chemical engineering concepts as they now are, do not require anything like the amount of manual work per unit of output. This trend goes on today. As an example, may I give the distillation load on one unit of the chemical industry. From 0.3m. tons a year before the war it increased to ·66m. tons soon after the end of the war. Today the load is 2.66m. tons a year.

One outstanding result of this trend has an important social bearing. It has given us a different type of workman. Today's process man has a much higher place in the social scale, and he is something much closer to a white-collared worker, with all that that implies. Another social implication is that the ratio in numbers between the relatively skilled process man and the highly trained, well-educated staff people (in the colleges' sense of the term) has gone up in respect to the latter. Thirty years ago one staff to six others was the kind of usual ratio in the industry. Today one to two is by no means abnormal, and one to one in certain branches is not unknown. All this means that the products of the industry are on the average far more sophisticated than they used to be, and of course more valuable for each unit of weight. The gross output of the chemical industry, as free as possible of duplicated values and broadly as defined in an earlier paragraph, is of the order of £900m. a year. Of this production some £195m. or 22 per cent is exported from the United Kingdom. The chemical industry is third in the Board of Trade figures of exporting industries.

The rate of exchange in chemical processes and products may well be among the highest for world industries. This means that for those countries that are striving after the introduction, or even the extension, of industrialization there are many reasons why the chemical industry is attractive. For this reason, we in Great Britain cannot expect to continue the export of the same products in ever-increasing quantities. From time to time we shall be called on to export our processes; but we hope that the total value of exports will continue to increase annually because of the introduction of new products and of old products in new forms. For the industry today the great need is for ever more well-founded scientific imagination, more skilled manipulation and more fundamental knowledge, all based on well-

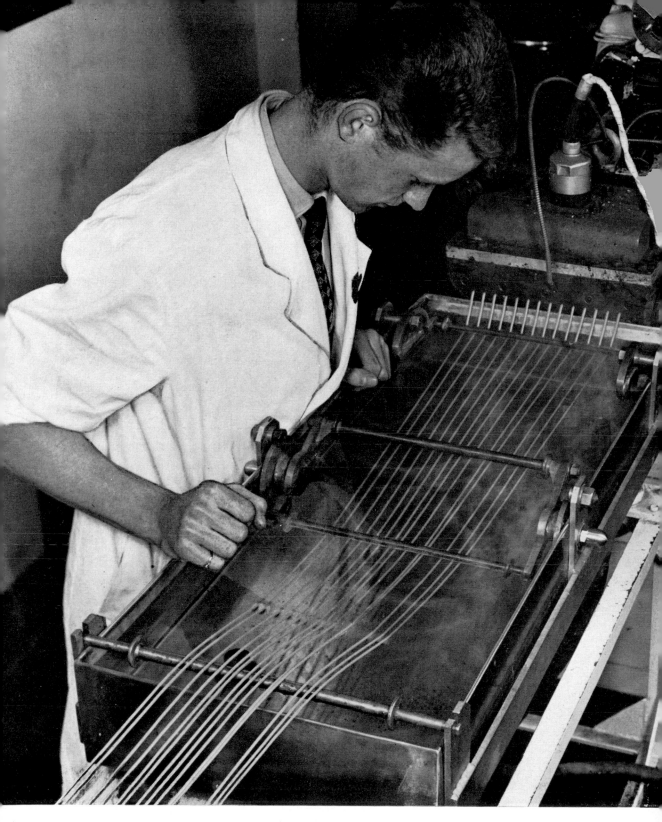

A 14-strand polyethylene extruder in one of the laboratories at Grangemouth.

Huge spheres for storing butadiene of British Hydrocarbon Chemicals at Grangemouth, Stirlingshire.

conceived research and development.

We look to the Royal Society, which has contributed so much in the past, for continued inspiration in chemical science. The chemical industry, however, does not concentrate its attention solely on chemical science. To maintain its prominent place in the world of progressive industries it must keep itself informed about advancing knowledge in all disciplines, and if it fails to use these advances for its processes and products it will do so at its peril. The Royal Society has given us leadership in the wide field that includes all branches of science. The chemical industry has benefited from that leadership and looks forward to receiving it with continuing effectiveness.

BELOW THE SURFACE OF ART

By F. I. G. Rawlins, C.B.E.

IT is only comparatively recently that interest has been awakened between the work of scientists and that of those devoted to the arts. This would not have seemed strange to the Greeks of the Golden Age, but it is accounted noteworthy today, when technology is sometimes supposed to have sharpened the line of demarcation. The frontier is often blurred, however. It is even possible to discern a certain reciprocity between the two subjects, suggesting interesting possibilities, which will be mentioned later on.

The most obvious connexion is the help that physics and chemistry can give to the study of art history. It is said that Von Roentgen had no sooner made his discovery of X-rays at the end of last century than he exposed a painting to them, to find out what lay beneath the surface. The result of this early experiment is not known, but the principle is in common use today. Its limitations should nevertheless be borne in mind. The method has little to say on question of style; modifications and alterations of original design are not

infrequently revealed, and these may well be of significance in historical research. Much the same applies to the use of infra-red photography. Here matters are simpler, in that it is a reflection rather than a transmission technique, and the image is not complicated by the presence of the support —wood or canvas, or whatever it may be.

Micro-analytical and microscopical processes have been developed, which are effective for minute portions of material. Here the purpose is not only identification but also to see how components are arranged relatively to each other, and thus, in favourable cases, to deduce how the object was constructed, and perhaps even its approximate date and provenance.

Another analytical means is that of chromatography. By this ingenious method (briefly, the recognition of stains in a certain order on filter papers) much has been learnt about the composition of the natural resins, and the vehicle, or medium, of old paint films.

Wall-paintings, ceramics and similar arts have been investigated by these means,

BELOW THE SURFACE OF ART

By F. I. G. Rawlins, C.B.E.

IT is only comparatively recently that interest has been awakened between the work of scientists and that of those devoted to the arts. This would not have seemed strange to the Greeks of the Golden Age, but it is accounted noteworthy today, when technology is sometimes supposed to have sharpened the line of demarcation. The frontier is often blurred, however. It is even possible to discern a certain reciprocity between the two subjects, suggesting interesting possibilities, which will be mentioned later on.

The most obvious connexion is the help that physics and chemistry can give to the study of art history. It is said that Von Roentgen had no sooner made his discovery of X-rays at the end of last century than he exposed a painting to them, to find out what lay beneath the surface. The result of this early experiment is not known, but the principle is in common use today. Its limitations should nevertheless be borne in mind. The method has little to say on question of style; modifications and alterations of original design are not infrequently revealed, and these may well be of significance in historical research. Much the same applies to the use of infra-red photography. Here matters are simpler, in that it is a reflection rather than a transmission technique, and the image is not complicated by the presence of the support —wood or canvas, or whatever it may be.

Micro-analytical and microscopical processes have been developed, which are effective for minute portions of material. Here the purpose is not only identification but also to see how components are arranged relatively to each other, and thus, in favourable cases, to deduce how the object was constructed, and perhaps even its approximate date and provenance.

Another analytical means is that of chromatography. By this ingenious method (briefly, the recognition of stains in a certain order on filter papers) much has been learnt about the composition of the natural resins, and the vehicle, or medium, of old paint films.

Wall-paintings, ceramics and similar arts have been investigated by these means,

Examining a radiograph of the head of the Virgin from " Madonna and Child Enthroned " on an illuminated viewing screen.

and their conservation facilitated. Today the search for the perfect varnish is perhaps the most intensive study in museum and gallery laboratories. The influence of solar and ultra-violet radiation is also receiving attention.

A matter of great consequence to art-lovers is the control of the environment in which precious material has to " live ". This is a problem for applied physics, and on its solution depends how long our patrimony may be expected to last in a polluted atmosphere. The introduction of air-conditioning has proved most beneficial, and should prolong the existence of our great collections almost indefinitely. In

162

addition to air-washing, this kind of control reduces considerably the strains resulting from the alternating intake and output of moisture that objects suffer with the periodic cycle of the seasons.

The give-and-take to which reference was made at the beginning is shown by the study of symbolic forms, a domain early cultivated by the mathematicians and illustrated in plant morphology. The presence of certain symmetry relations and tangential properties—at key points of an object—are fundamental for abstract art, and in certain combinations are conducive to aesthetic pleasure. This is a region wherein the concepts of spatial geometry and sculpture may find common ground.

Mr. Rawlins engaged in research on the physics of painting at the National Gallery. Here he looks at picture under a low-power binocular microscope.

MAN'S OLDEST CRAFT MODERNIZED

By Sir William Slater, K.B.E., F.R.S.

AGRICULTURE, man's oldest craft, evolved its techniques over many centuries by trial and error. It was only after the birth of experimental science that there arose the desire first to record and explain the traditional methods of the husbandman, and then to improve and develop them. The first serious contribution to agricultural science was presented as a discourse to the Royal Society in 1675, when Evelyn spoke of " Earth, relating to the culture and improvement of it for Vegetation and the propagation of Plants "; this discourse was published on the instructions of the council of the Royal Society. From then onwards scientists began to build up knowledge in the descriptive sciences that was to prove invaluable for the future development of agricultural practice.

The history of agriculture in the 120 years that followed Evelyn's discourse is marked by the names of great pioneers—men like Townsend, Tull, Coke and Bakewell—but they were essentially prac-

tical farmers applying any scientific knowledge available to them; the scientist had not then developed the techniques that would enable him to study the problems of agriculture by planned experiment. It was left to Humphry Davy at the end of the eighteenth century, then a young man working at the Royal Institution, to apply the rapidly developing knowledge of chemistry to the study of agriculture.

The evolution of organic chemistry in the first half of the nineteenth century enabled Liebig and his co-worker to carrys these studies much further, and to show the important part that chemistry could play in explaining the plant/soil relationship and the phenomena involved in plant growth. Perhaps more important still, they developed and expanded the quantitative experimental methods that had been first introduced by de Saussure. In this country Gilbert, who had worked with and been inspired by Liebig, joined forces with Lawes—a land-owner and the in-

John Bennet Lawes (1814–1900), founder and financier of the world's first institution for agricultural research at Rothamsted.

ventor of the process for making superphosphate—to found at Rothamsted the first institution in the world devoted solely to agricultural research. The rapidly expanding urban industry of the nineteenth century maintained for many years an agriculture that prospered on its traditional methods; thus, while agriculture appeared to have little need for science, the manufacturing industries of the towns began to clamour for its help.

When cheap imports destroyed the earlier prosperity, it was generally assumed that little could be done to maintain British agriculture. There was, however, a group of scientists and teachers, such men as Middleton, Hall, Bateson and Russell, who believed in the need for a healthy home agriculture and the help that science could give in creating it. Their efforts made possible the expansion of agricultural research following the bitter lessons of the First World War. The embryonic institutes already existing were expanded and new ones established, until once again the depression of the thirties brought all development of research to a standstill. It was not until a new threat of war and famine arose that the need to continue the expansion of research was again recognized. Since then, this need has never been questioned. Even in the most difficult days of the war facilities were made available for research and for the application of the results in farming practice.

In 1946 the Agricultural Research

PLOT 3.
NO
MANURE.

PLOT 6.
MINERALS
+
200 LBS. S/AM.

PLOT 7.
MINERALS
+
400 LBS. S/AM.

PLOT 8.
MINERALS
+
600 LBS. S/AM.

Sheaves of wheat showing the effects of increased nitrogen fertilizer treatments.

Council was instructed to draw up a 10-year plan for expanding the research effort to cover all branches of agriculture. More than was then planned has been achieved; the pattern has had to be changed to meet changing needs, but the total expansion in manpower, buildings and equipment has been greater than was envisaged. In all this expansion the chief brake on progress has been not shortage of funds but of trained men. In 1947-48 the amount spent by the state on agricultural research was of the order of £1m., today it is almost £6,500,000. In the same period the scientific staff of the research institutes and units, which now includes more than 20 fellows of the Royal Society, has doubled.

The output of work has increased in proportion and its breadth has been expanded. The direct attack on agricultural problems, which proved so successful in

166

SYLVA,

Or A DISCOURSE Of

FOREST-TREES,

AND THE

Propagation of Timber

In His MAJESTIES Dominions.

By *J. E.* Esq;

As it was Deliver'd in the *ROYAL SOCIETY* the xv[th] of
October, CIƆIƆCLXII. upon Occasion of certain *Quæries*
Propounded to that *Illustrious Assembly,* by the *Honorable* the Principal
Officers, and *Commissioners* of the *Navy.*

To which is annexed
POMONA Or, An *Appendix* concerning *Fruit-Trees* in relation to *CIDER*;
The *Making* and several ways of *Ordering* it.

Published by express Order of the *ROYAL SOCIETY.*

ALSO
KALENDARIUM HORTENSE; Or, *Gard'ners Almanac*;
Directing *what he is to do Monethly* throughout the *Year.*

—————*Tibi res antiquæ laudis & artis*
Ingredior, tantos ausus recludere fonteis. Virg.

NVLLIVS IN VERBA

LONDON, Printed by *Jo. Martyn,* and *Ja. Allestry,* Printers to the *Royal
Society,* and are to be sold at their Shop at the *Bell* in S. *Paul's* Church-yard,
MDCLXIV.

The front page of one of the earliest treatises on agriculture by John Evelyn,
published in 1664.

Preparing a lecture exhibit of Rothamsted showing the effect of various fertilizers on barley.

the early stages, is no longer enough. In every branch of work, in soil chemistry, plant and animal physiology, genetics, bacteriology and virology, to name only some of the disciplines involved, the need is for information of a fundamental character about the many factors that control the growth and reproduction of plants and animals. While field experiments still play their valuable part, much of the work must be done under conditions of controlled environment; the simple laboratory equipment of the thirties has been replaced by the wide range of new and elaborate apparatus required for the more precise and detailed measurements that are essential.

Although it is difficult to attribute to any one particular investigation an immediate rise in farming efficiency, there is no doubt that the combined effect of the results of the many has had a profound influence on production. The steady increase in the yields of cereals has come from the breeding of better varieties, the development of methods for controlling

J. B. Lawes's earliest experiment, started in 1843, was to divide a field into five parts and allow one part to lie fallow each year, resulting in an improved crop.

diseases and weed competition, and from a fuller knowledge of fertilizer response. The increase in the milk production of our dairy herds, which are giving an increasing total yield from fewer animals, follows from the application of scientific knowledge to feeding, nutrition and disease control. Tuberculosis has been almost eradicated from our cattle, contagious abortion may soon follow, and many of the diseases that used to decimate our sheep flock can now be controlled.

Each advance opens up new vistas of progress, but at the same time creates new problems. The high level of production that is now expected by the better farmers from their livestock is bringing in its train nutritional diseases, the causes of which must be found and means of prevention provided. Crop production on our best farms has now reached a level where every contributing factor must be kept at the same high standard of efficiency if the whole process is to be economically sound. There is a constant demand for better varieties, more efficient weed and pest control and more precise information on fertilizer practice.

Science has brought about a revolution in agriculture in the past two decades; work now in progress in the laboratories gives every promise for continued progress in the future.

ADAPTING THE VULGAR TONGUE

By Theodore Savory

IN the beginning the Royal Society published the papers of its Fellows in either Latin or English. The encouragement of the vulgar tongue for intellectual work was something of an innovation, and contributors to the now famous *Philosophical Transactions* were requested to use "a close, naked, natural way of Speaking; positive expressions, clear senses; a native easiness".

But the description of newly discovered facts and the expression of newly conceived ideas demand words that, at the time of writing, do not exist. Language has always failed to keep pace with the development of human thought, and scientists, like other scholars, have been forced to create their own vocabulary as their work progressed. They have, in general, followed three courses.

Most simply, they borrowed words from ordinary speech, giving them new definitions, to justify their new uses. Only in physics does moment imply the product of force by distance; only in chemistry is a base the oxide or hydroxide of a metal.

Occasionally it has happened that the scientists' new use of a word has suppressed its original meaning; no one today thinks of dialysis, efflorescence or parasite with any but their later, scientific, meanings.

The second method was to import a word from a foreign tongue and use it, unchanged, in its original sense. This is not confined to science: hundreds of our words, from potato and earlier to sputnik and later, have thus entered our language. From the Renaissance the Latin dictionary and Greek Lexicon were open to our writers, and none more enthusiastically exploited the opportunity than the scientists. Focus and pollen, nectar, stigma and nucleus, with unnumbered others, belong to this category. From classical roots, moreover, sprang the true words of science, words invented by the scientists themselves when their needs could not be met in any other way. The number of such words has grown at an ever-increasing rate for the past 300 years; many have become familiar to all—vitamin, paraffin, cathode, isotope—and many more may never be used outside the writings of the scientists— telolecithal, stenohaline, parachor. These words have definite characteristics. They are adequately defined from the first, they are usually accepted by other scientists, and above all they seldom suffer that change of meaning which, by the accretion of associations, is the fate of so many ordinary words.

The words of science build up into a language with a character of its own. It is a language of great stability. Since the meanings of its words do not change, the language itself does not evolve as does the writing of men of letters: it has few synonyms, so that much of its doctrine is expounded in universally similar terms. It is a language of remarkable clarity. By those who are familiar with the words in it, a scientific paragraph can scarcely be misunderstood. That it may seem to be obscure to some readers is a result of the specialization of all recent science, not a result of obscurity of language. In this respect the language of science has been compared to mathematical formulae, which are written not in words but in generally accepted symbols.

Because of its clarity, precision, and constancy, the language of science is cold, plain, and forthright. No warmth of human emotion, no grace of literary decoration, no touch of humour, no shamed euphemism, no eloquence is found in its composition. It is, and it is likely to remain, a language within a language, serving no more than its own purposes; yet, as science more thoroughly permeates our daily lives, more and more must men and women come to read and write the language of the laboratory.

THE ROYAL SOCIETY

PATRON
Queen Elizabeth II.

ROYAL FELLOWS

The Duke of Edinburgh, K.G., K.T.	..	..	..	..	1951
Queen Elizabeth The Queen Mother.	..	..	..	..	1956
The Duke of Gloucester, K.G., K.T., K.P.	..	..	..	..	1938
The Duke of Windsor, K.G., K.T., K.P.	..	..	..	..	1919
King Gustav VI Adolf of Sweden, K.G.	..	..	..	..	1959

THE COUNCIL 1960

THE PRESIDENT
Sir Cyril Hinshelwood

TREASURER AND VICE-PRESIDENT
Sir William Penney

SECRETARIES AND VICE-PRESIDENTS
Sir Lindor Brown
Sir William Hodge

FOREIGN SECRETARY AND VICE-PRESIDENT
Sir Gerald Thornton

VICE-PRESIDENTS
Sir Patrick Linstead
Professor W. Smith

Professor J. F. Baker	Dr. R. A. Lyttleton
Dr. J. C. Burkill	Sir Harrie Massey
Professor D. G. Catcheside	Professor R. A. Morton
Professor T. M. Harris	Sir Alfred Pugsley
Professor L. Hawkes	Professor R. J. Pumphrey
Professor A. L. Hodgkin	Dr. H. W. Thompson
Dame Kathleen Lonsdale	Professor J. Z. Young

FELLOWS

1904
Professor M. W. Travers.

1906
Professor H. A. Wilson.

1908
Lord Russell, O.M.

1911
Professor W. H. Lang.

1912
Professor R. C. Punnett.

1913
Professor V. H. Blackman.
Professor T. R. Elliott, C.B.E., D.S.O.

1914
Sir Henry Dale, O.M., G.B.E. (Past President).
Sir Thomas Havelock.

1915
Sir George Simpson, K.C.B., C.B.E.

1916
Professor J. E. Littlewood.
Sir Leonard Rogers, K.C.S., C.I.E.

1917
Sir Leonard Bairstow, C.B.E.
Sir John Russell, O.B.E.

1918
Mr. E. Gold, C.B., D.S.O., O.B.E.
Professor A. V. Hill, C.H., O.B.E.
Sir Frank Smith, G.C.B., G.B.E.

1919
Professor S. Chapman.
Sir Geoffrey Taylor.
Dr. G. N. Watson.

1920
Sir Thomas Merton, K.B.E.
Sir Robert Robinson, O.M. (Past President).

1921
Sir Lawrence Bragg, O.B.E.
Dr. W. H. Eccles.

1922
Sir Charles Darwin, K.B.E., M.C.
Professor C. G. Douglas, C.M.G., M.C., D.M.
Professor D. M. S. Watson.

1923
Lord Adrian, O.M. (Past President).
Dr. W. L. Balls, C.M.G., C.B.E.
Professor R. T. Leiper, C.M.G.
Professor W. Wilson.

1924
Sir Christopher Ingold.
Professor L. J. Mordell.
Sir Venkata Raman.

1925
Sir Charles Lovatt Evans.
Dr. F. A. Freeth, O.B.E.
Sir Harold Jeffries.
Professor J. Kenner.
Professor J. Proudman, C.B.E.
Sir Richard Southwell.
Professor R. Whiddington, C.B.E.

1926

Sir Rickard Christophers, C.I.E., O.B.E.
Sir Harold Hartley, G.C.V.O., C.B.E., M.C.
Professor H. Hartridge.
Dr. E. Griffiths, O.B.E.
Professor O. T. Jones.

1927

Sir Edward Appleton, G.B.E., K.C.B.
Professor T. G. Brown.
Sir James Chadwick.
Dr. G. M. B. Dobson, C.B.E.
Professor J. Kendall.
Lord Stopford, K.B.E.

1928

Professor C. H. Browning.
Professor J. W. H. Harrison.
Professor D. Keilin.
Professor W. Stiles.

1929

Sir Charles Ellis.
Sir Ronald Fisher.
Professor G. R. Goldsbrough, C.B.E.
Sir James Gray, C.B.E., M.C.
Sir Cyril Hinshelwood, O.M. (President).
Academician P. Kapitza.
Dr. W. D. Lang.
Sir Harry Ricardo.

1930

Sir Edward Bailey, M.C.
Professor P. A. M. Dirac.
Sir Harold Spencer Jones, K.B.E.
Sir Eric Rideal, M.B.E.
Sir George Thomson.

1931

Professor P. G. H. Boswell.
Mr. C. R. Davidson.
Professor R. R. Gates.
Sir Charles Harington.
Professor E. C. Titchmarsh.

1932

Sir Frederick Bartlett, C.B.E.
Lord Boyd-Orr, D.S.O., M.C.
Professor W. G. Fearnsides.
Professor J. A. Gray, O.B.E.
Professor J. B. S. Haldane.
Dr. F. R. Miller.
Mr. T. Smith.
Sir Hugh Taylor, K.B.E.
Professor H. W. Turnbull.

1933

Professor P. M. S. Blackett.
Professor J. B. Collip, C.B.E.
Dr. A. T. Doodson, C.B.E.
Dr. H. J. Gough, C.B., M.B.E.
Sir John Hammond, C.B.E.
Sir Gordon Holmes, C.M.G., C.B.E.
Dr. J. W. McLeod, O.B.E.
Dr. A. S. Parkes, C.B.E.
Sir Edward Salisbury, C.B.E.
Dr. W. R. Thompson.
Professor A. M. Tyndall, C.B.E.

1934

Professor A. S. Besicovitch.
Professor W. E. Curtis.
Sir Paul Fildes, O.B.E.
Dr. R. T. Grant, O.B.E.
Mr. M. A. C. Hinton.
Professor E. L. Hirst, C.B.E.
Professor H. Raistrick.
Dr. R. B. S. Sewell, C.I.E.
Dr. H. H. Thomas, M.B.E.

1935

Professor N. K. Adam.
Professor E. N. da C. Andrade.
Sir Samuel Bedson.
Dr. E. J. Bowen.
Professor G. E. Briggs.
Professor H. G. Cannon.
Sir Wilfred Le Gros Clark.
Professor J. S. Foster.
Dr. J. de Graaff-Hunter, C.I.E.
Sir Bernard Keen.
Sir Rudolph Peters, M.C.
Professor J. Read.
Dr. R. Stoneley.

1936

Professor A. C. Aitken.
Professor E. B. Verney.
Sir John Cockcroft, O.M., K.C.B., C.B.E.
Professor H. J. Fleure.
Professor L. Hogben.
Dr. J. Kenyon.
Professor N. F. Mott.
Professor R. G. W. Norrish.
Professor H. H. Plaskett.
Mr. E. F. Relf, C.B.E.
Professor F. J. W. Roughton.

1937

Professor J. D. Bernal.
Professor A. C. Chibnall.
Professor G. R. Clemo.
Sir Alan Drury, C.B.E.
Professor H. M. Fox.
Professor S. Goldstein.
Professor H. L. Hawkins.
Professor W. Hume-Rothery, O.B.E.
Professor C. F. A. Pantin.
Sir Marcus Oliphant, K.B.E.
Professor E. C. Stoner.

1938

Professor C. H. Best, C.B.E.
Professor W. Brown.
Dr. J. W. Cook.
Professor G. I. Finch, M.B.E.
Sir William Hodge.
Sir Julian Huxley.
Dr. J. E. Richey, M. C.
Dr. F. S. Russell, C.B.E., D.F.C., D.S.C.
Sir Basil Schonland, C.B.E.
Dr. K. M. Smith, C.B.E.
Dr. E. Stedman.
Professor C. E. Tilley.
Professor W. E. S. Turner, O.B.E.

1939

Mr. G. S. Adair.
Dr. C. H. Andrewes.
Professor M. Born.
Dr. A. J. Bradley.
Sir David Brunt, K.B.E.
Professor F. A. E. Crew.
Sir Melvill Jones, C.B.E., A.F.C.
Professor E. G. T. Liddell.
Sir Irvine Masson, M.B.E.
Dr. C. E. K. Mees.
Professor M. H. A. Newmann.
Lord Nuffield, G.B.E., C.H.
Professor H. H. Read.
Sir George Stapleton, C.B.E.
Professor E. E. Turner.
Professor V. B. Wigglesworth, C.B.E.

1940

Professor W. T. Astbury.
Sir Gavin de Beer.
Professor O. M. B. Bulman.
Professor H. Davenport.
Sir Charles Goodeve, O.B.E.
Professor F. G. Gregory.

176

Sir Kariamanikkam Krishnan.
Sir Patrick Linstead, C.B.E.
Dr. O. Maass, C.B.E.
Sir Harrie Massey.
Sir Bryan Matthews, C.B.E.
Professor W. H. Pearsall.
Professor J. H. Quastel.
Dr. A. Robertson.
Professor W. Sucksmith.

1941

Dr. H. J. Bhabha.
Sir Edward Bullard.
Rt. Hon. Sir Winston Churchill, K.G.,
    O.M., C.H., M.P.
Professor C. D. Darlington.
Professor P. I. Dee, C.B.E.
Sir John Eccles.
Sir Howard Florey.
Dr. A. A. Griffith, C.B.E.
Sir Harry Melville, K.C.B.
Dr. J. Needham.
Sir David Rivett, K.C.M.G.
Professor A. Robertson.
Professor T. G. Room.
Dr. H. Scott.
Sir Gerald Thornton.
Sir Robert Watson-Watt, C.B.

1942

Professor J. H. Burn.
Sir Macfarlane Burnet, O.M.
Dr. M. Dixon.
Sir Charles Dodds, M.V.O.
Mr. A. Fage, C.B.E.
Sir Neil Hamilton Fairley, K.B.E.
Professor P. Hall.
Professor C. S. Hanes.
Lord Hankey, G.C.B., G.C.M.G.,
    G.C.V.O.
Professor T. P. Hilditch, C.B.E.

Dr. E. Hindle.
Professor A. Holmes.
Professor D. M. Newitt, M.C.
Professor D. Thoday.
Sir Alexander Todd.
Dr. A. H. Wilson.

1943

Dr. I. de B. Daly, C.B.E.
Vice-Admiral Sir John Edgell, K.B.E., C.B.
Professor S. C. Harland.
Sir Andrew McCance.
Dr. W. Penfield, O.M., C.M.G.
Dr. C. Sykes, C.B.E.
Professor J. L. Synge.
Professor G. Temple, C.B.E.
Sir Solly Zuckerman, C.B.

1944

Brigadier R. A. Bagnold, O.B.E.
Mr. R. P. Bell.
Lord Bruce of Melbourne, P.C., C.H., M.C.
Dr. C. R. Burch, C.B.E.
Professor S. Chandrasekhar.
Dr. G. E. R. Deacon, C.B.E.
Mr. A. T. Glenny.
Sir Ronald Hatton, C.B.E.
Professor R. D. Haworth.
Professor W. O. Kermack.
Dr. F. Kidd, C.B.E.
Dr. G. F. Marrian.
Professor M. Polanyi.
Sir William Stanier.
Dr. C. J. Stubblefield.

1945

Sir William Farren, C.B., M.B.E.
Dr. L. Colebrook.
Professor N. Feather.
Dr. J. H. Gaddum.

Dr. H. Godwin.
Dr. H. W. Harvey, C.B.E.
Professor V. C. Illing.
Mr. A. E. Ingham.
Professor H. D. Kay, C.B.E.
Dr. W. B. Lewis, C.B.E.
Dame Kathleen Lonsdale, D.B.E.
Professor P. C. Mahalanobis.
Professor R. E. Peierls, C.B.E.
Professor J. M. Robertson.
Dr. B. N. Wallis, C.B.E.
Professor J. Z. Young.

1946

Professor W. Baker.
Sir Lindor Brown, C.B.E.
Sir Roy Cameron.
Professor F. Dickens.
Professor H. J. Eméleus, C.B.E.
Sir Frank Engledow, C.M.G.
Dr. E. B. Ford.
Professor E. A. Guggenheim.
Sir Ronald Hatton, C.B.E.
Dr. R. Hill.
Dr. C. J. Mackenzie, C.M.G., M.C.
Sir Ernest Marsden, C.M.G., C.B.E., M.C.
Sir William Penney, K.B.E.
Professor J. T. Randall.
Professor R. O. Redman.
Professor L. Rosenhead, C.B.E.
Dr. H. H. Storey, C.M.G.
Dr. H. W. Thompson, C.B.E.
Professor L. R. Wager.
Sir Francis Walshe, O.B.E.
Professor C. M. Yonge, C.B.E.

1947

Lord Attlee, K.G., O.M., C.H.
Mr. W. S. Bisat.

Dr. Mary Cartwright.
Professor E. J. Conway.
Professor T. G. Cowling.
Dr. J. Craigie, O.B.E.
Mr. M. B. Crane.
Professor W. J. Duncan, C.B.E.
Professor W. S. Feldberg.
Dr. Dorothy M. C. Hodgkin.
Dr. J. Hutchinson.
Dr. D. A. Jackson, O.B.E., D.F.C., A.F.C.
Sir Geoffrey Jefferson, C.B.E.
Sir Hans Krebs.
Professor P. B. Moon.
Dr. F. G. Mann.
Professor E. Orowan.
Dr. Muriel Robertson.
Professor F. J. M. Stratton, D.S.O., O.B.E.
Professor C. H. Waddington, C.B.E.
Sir Frank Whittle, K.B.E., C.B.

1948

Dr. T. E. Allibone, C.B.E.
Dr. F. P. Bowden, C.B.E.
Mr. H. Constant, C.B., C.B.E.
Dr. S. F. Dorey, C.B.E.
Professor O. R. Frisch, O.B.E.
Professor T. M. Harris.
Professor W. H. Heitler.
Professor A. L. Hodgkin.
Professor R. A. McCance, C.B.E.
Professor K. Mahler.
Dr. Sidnie Manton.
Dr. Dorothy M. M. Needham.
Professor S. Peat.
Mr. J. W. Ryde.
Mr. R. Snow.
Dr. E. W. R. Steacie, O.B.E.
Dr. J. A. Todd.
Dr. F. Yates.
Dr. W. A. H. Rushton.
Professor J. F. Allen.

1949

Mr. F. C. Bawden.
Professor F. W. R. Brambell.
Professor K. E. Bullen.
Professor E. B. Chain.
Dr. U. R. Evans.
Professor E. D. Hughes.
Professor W. Q. Kennedy.
Professor W. B. R. King, O.B.E., M.C.
Sir Ben Lockspeiser, K.C.B.
Sir James McNeill, K.C.V.O., C.B.E., M.C.
Mr. H. R. Marston.
Professor K. Mather, C.B.E.
Professor W. T. J. Morgan, C.B.E.
Mr. N. W. Pirie.
Professor C. F. Powell.
Dr. D. A. Scott.
Professor W. Smith.
Sir Gordon Sutherland, Kt.
Sir Graham Sutton, C.B.E.
Professor M. Thomas.
Dr. J. M. Whittaker.
Professor F. G. Young.

1950

Professor L. F. Bates.
Professor T. A. Bennet-Clark.
Professor B. Bleaney.
Professor C. A. Coulson.
Dr. L. R. Cox, O.B.E.
Professor H. S. M. Coxeter.
Dr. G. H. Cunningham, C.B.E.
Mr. S. B. Gates, O.B.E.
Dr. C. A. Hoare.
Professor L. Howarth, O.B.E.
Professor E. R. H. Jones.
Dr. A. J. P. Martin, C.B.E.
Dr. D. F. Martyn.
Professor R. A. Morton.
Professor R. J. Pumphrey.

Professor A. G. Shenstone, O.B.E., M.C.
Col. H. E. Shortt, C.I.E.
Professor M. Stacey.
Dr. L. E. Sutton.
Dr. R. L. M. Synge.
Dr. G. M. Trevelyan, O.M.
Dr. B. P. Uvarov, C.M.G.
Professor F. C. Williams, O.B.E.

1951

Dr. C. S. Beals.
Brigadier Sir John Boyd, O.B.E.
Professor D. G. Catcheside.
Dr. A. H. Cook.
Dr. S. J. Folley.
Professor H. Fröhlich.
Professor G. Gee, C.B.E.
Professor H. A. Heilbronn.
Dr. G. Herzberg.
Sir Joseph Hutchinson, C.M.G.
Dr. H. R. Ing.
Dr. D. Lack.
Dr. T. R. R. Mann.
Dr. K. A. G. Mendelssohn.
Professor A. Neuberger.
Dr. L. B. Pfeil, O.B.E.
Professor J. A. Prescott, C.B.E.
Professor M. H. L. Pryce.
Sir William Pugh, O.B.E.
Mr. J. A. Ratcliffe, C.B.E.
Professor T. A. Stephenson.
Dr. W. H. Thorpe.
Dr. P. J. du Toit.
Professor A. R. J. P. Ubbelohde.

1952

Professor C. E. H. Bawn, C.B.E.
Professor N. J. Berrill.
Lord Bridges, P.C., G.C.B., G.C.V.O.,
    M.C.

Mr. J. H. Craigie.
Professor F. J. Dyson.
Dr. Honor B. Fell.
Dr. D. L. Hammick.
Professor L. Hawkes.
Professor W. O. James.
Professor H. Jones.
Professor B. Katz.
Dr. M. R. Lemberg.
Professor W. H. McCrea.
Professor J. S. Mitchell, C.B.E.
Professor A. C. Offord.
Sir Alfred Pugsley, O.B.E.
Dr. R. R. Race.
Professor M. Ryle.
Dr. D. M. Smith.
Dr. F. S. Spring.
Dr. E. W. Taylor, C.B.E.
Professor S. Tolansky.
Dr. Marthe L. Vogt.
Professor T. S. Westcoll.
Professor D. D. Woods.

1953

Dr. J. S. Anderson.
Dr. K. Bailey.
Professor H. Barcroft.
Dr. J. Barker.
Dr. J. C. Burkill.
Dr. J. W. Cornforth.
Dr. S. C. Curran.
Mr. C. S. Elton.
Dr. O.H. Frankel.
Dr. E. F. Gale.
Dr. A. G. Gaydon.
Sir Arnold Hall.
Professor G. W. Harris.
Sir Claude Inglis, C.I.E.
Sir Willis Jackson.
Mr. M. J. Lighthill.
Dr. G. H. Mitchell.

Professor L. S. Penrose.
Mr. A. R. Powell.
Mr. H. M. Powell.
Lord Rothschild, G.M.
Dr. D. Shoenberg, M.B.E.
Professor T. Wallace, C.B.E., M.C.
Professor D. Whitteridge.
Dr. R. van der R. Woolley, O.B.E.

1954

Professor D. H. R. Barton.
Professor T. M. Cherry.
Professor E. G. Cox.
Professor F. C. Frank, O.B.E.
Professor A. B. Hill, C.B.E.
Professor E. S. Hills.
Sir Christopher Hinton, K.B.E.
Dr. F. E. King.
Dr. H. G. Kuhn.
Dr. H. W. Lissman.
Professor F. C. MacIntosh.
Dr. L. H. Matthews.
Dr. J. L. Pawsey.
Dr. M. F. Perutz.
Professor A. J. S. Pippard, M.B.E.
Dr. Rosalind V. Pitt-Rivers.
Professor R. D. Preston.
Dr. J. W. S. Pringle, M.B.E.
Dr. F. J. Richards.
Professor C. Rimmington.
Dr. W. W. Rogosinski.
Dr. F. Sanger.
Dr. H. G. Thode.
Dr. W. A. Waters.
Dr. C. B. Williams.

1955

Professor D. R. Bates.
Mr. E. J. H. Corner.
Professor A. H. Cottrell.

Professor S. Devons.
Professor A. W. Downie.
Professor K. C. Dunham.
Dr. D. J. Finney.
Sir Alexander Fleck, K.B.E.
Professor K. J. Franklin.
Professor W. R. Hawthorne, C.B.E.
Professor D. H. Hey.
Sir Harold Himsworth, K.C.B.
Mr. A. F. Huxley.
Professor R. W. James.
Professor D. Lewis.
Dr. J. W. Linett.
Professor A. C. B. Lovell, O.B.E.
Professor O. E. Lowenstein.
Dr. R. A. Lyttleton.
Professor A. G. Ogston.
Professor G. Pontecorvo.
Dr. J. A. Ramsay.
Professor F. C. Tompkins.
Professor A. G. Walker.
Professor G. P. Wells.

1956

Dr. N. P. Allen.
Professor J. F. Baker, O.B.E.
Professor R. M. Barrer.
Professor R. Brown.
Professor J. A. V. Butler.
Professor D. Gabor.
Professor H. Gruneberg.
Mr. C. S. Hallpike, C.B.E.
Professor J. E. Harris.
Professor W. K. Hayman.
Professor N. Kemmer.
Dr. N. Kurti.
Dr. R. Markham.
Dr. R. G. MacFarlane.
Dr. J. W. Mitchell.
Professor W. D. M. Paton.

Professor A. B. Pippard, M.B.E.
Professor Helen K. Porter.
Dr. G. Salt.
Professor C. W. Shoppee.
Professor F. W. Shotton, M.B.E.
Dr. E. I. White, C.B.E.
Mr. M. V. Wilkes.
Professor D. H. Wilkinson.
Professor A. Wormall.

1957

Professor S. Alder, O.B.E.
Professor E. C. Amoroso.
Dr. Charlotte Auerbach.
Dr. G. K. Batchelor.
Professor W. E. Burcham.
Professor F. S. Dainton.
Professor J. F. Danielli.
Sir Alister Hardy.
Professor F. Hoyle.
Professor J. K. N. Jones.
Professor H. S. Lipsom.
Professor J. McMichael.
Sir Leslie Martin, C.B.E.
Professor C. L. Oakley.
Professor H. R. Pitt.
Dr. F. L. Rose, O.B.E.
Lord Salisbury, K.G., P.C.
Sir William Slater, K.B.E.
Dr. E. Lester Smith.
Sir Ewart Smith.
Professor H. B. Squire.
Professor F. C. Steward.
Dr. W. S. Stiles, O.B.E.
Dr. R. C. Sutcliffe, O.B.E.
Dr. D. N. Wadia.
Dr. A. S. Watt.
Professor W. F. Whittard.

1958

Professor M. Abercrombie.
Dr. E. P. Abraham.

181

Dr. J. R. Baker.
Professor A. J. Birch.
Professor S. Bose.
Dr. P. W. Brian.
Dr. Edith Bülbring.
Dr. R. K. Callow.
Dr. F. Dixie, C.M.G., O.B.E.
Professor P. P. Ewald.
Professor F. I. Fenner, M.B.E.
Sir William H. Glanville, C.B., C.B.E.
Professor A. E. Green.
Professor A. Haddow.
Dr. G. Higman.
Professor A. St. G. J. M. Huggett.
Professor H. C. Longuet-Higgins.
Professor B. Lythgoe.
Professor S. K. Mitra.
Dr. C. H. Mortimer.
Professor R. S. Nyholm.
Professor G. D. Rochester.
Professor O. A. Saunders.
Professor J. E. Smith.
Dr. W. B. Turrill, O.B.E.

1959

Dr. G. H. Beale, M.B.E.
Professor F. Bergel.
Dr. Ann Bishop.
Professor G. E. Blackman.
Professor H. Bondi.
Professor J. M. Cassels.
Professor A. R. Clapham.
Dr. F. H. C. Crick.
Mr. G. B. R. Feilden.
Dr. D. W. W. Henderson, C. B.
Dr. R. D. Keynes.
Professor R. J. W. Le Fevre.
Dr. B. H. Neumann.

Dr. S. R. Nockolds.
Professor W. C. Price.
Professor G. V. Raynor.
Professor O. W. Richards.
Dr. R. E. Richards.
Professor C. A. Rogers.
Professor A. Salam.
Dr. R. Spence, C.B.
Dr. J. F. Tait.
Mrs. Sylvia A. S. Tait.
Dr. M. H. F. Wilkins.
Professor S. W. Wooldridge, C.B.E.

1960

Mr. A. M. Binnie.
Professor R. Hanbury Brown.
Professor D. G. Christopherson, O.B.E.
Professor R. H. Dalitz.
Professor J. N. Davidson.
Professor M. J. Dewar.
Sir Stewart Duke-Elder, G.C.V.O.
Dr. Louis Essen, O.B.E.
Dr. D. G. Evans.
Mr. N. L. Falcon.
Dr. P. A. Gorer.
Professor O. V. Heath.
Dr. R. Holroyd.
Dr. H. E. Huxley, M.B.E.
Dr. J. C. Kendrew, Ph.D.
Dr. J. A. Kitching, O.B.E.
Dr. D. K. C. Macdonald.
Sir George Pickering.
Professor G. Porter.
Dr. K. F. Roth.
Professor T. R. Sheshadri.
Professor J. H. Taylor.
Dr. A. A. Townsend.
Professor R. L. Wain.
Dr. E. N. Willmer.

FOREIGN MEMBERS

1916

Professor J. J. B. V. Bordet.

1926

Professor Neils Bohr.

1932

Professor J. Hadamard.

1933

Professor P. Debye.

1934

Professor O. H. Warburg.

1936

Professor F. A. Vening Meinesz.

1938

Professor N. E. Nörlund.

1939

Professor G. C. De Hevesy.

1940

Le Duc de Broglie.
Dr. F. P. Rous.

1941

Dr. J. B. Conant.

1942

Academician I. M. Vinogradov.
Professor L. Ruzicka.
Dr. A. N. Richards.

1943

Professor B. A. Houssay.

1944

Professor T. Svedberg.
Professor N. E. Svedelius.
Professor S. Timoshenko.

1946

Dr. H. S. Gasser.
Professor T. von Karman.
Professor E. A. Stensiö.

1947

Professor H. C. Urey.
Professor O. Wingc.
Professor P. Karrer.

1948

Dr. D. W. Bronk.
Professor L. E. J. Bronwer.
Professor L. C. Pauling.

1949

Professor E. Schrödinger.
Professor P. W. Bridgman.

1950

Professor C. F. Cori.
Professor C. J. F. Skottsberg.

1951

Dr. R. W. G. Wyckoff.
Professor H. M. Evans.

1952

Professor S. O. Hörstadius.
Professor A. M. G. R. Portevin.
Professor T. Reichstein.

1953

Professor H. J. Muller.
Professor M. J. C. R. Courrier.
Prince Louis de Broglie.

1954

Professor K. von Frisch.
Professor O. Loewi.
Professor K. M. G. Siegbahn.
Professor O. Struve.

1955

Professor W. Heisenberg.
Professor Lise Meitner.
Professor G. W. Corner.
Professor O. Renner.

1956

Professor H. Pettersson.
Professor F. Zernike.
Professor R. B. Woodward.

1957

Professor H. A. Bethe.
Professor A. Frey-Wyssling.
Professor O. Hahn.
Professor A. W. K. Tiselius.

1958

Professor A. Stoll.
Professor G. G. Simpson.
Academician N. N. Semenov.
Dr. A. M. Lwoff.

1959

Professor M. Calvin.
Professor G. Domagk.
Professor J. H. Oort.
Professor A. H. T. Theorell.

1960

Professor G. W. Beadle.
Professor R. A. Granit.
Professor G. B. Kistiakowsky.
Academician L. D. Landau.

FELLOWS OF
THE ROYAL SOCIETY
who have received the
ORDER OF MERIT

Lord Russell, 1949.

Sir Henry Dale, 1944.

Sir Edward Appleton, 1947.

Sir James Chadwick, 1935.

Sir Lawrence Bragg, 1915.

Professor Niels Bohr, 1922.

Lord Adrian, 1942.

NOBEL PRIZE WINNERS

The following Fellows of the Royal Society are Nobel Laureates:

Sir L. BRAGG, O.B.E. (Physics, 1915); Prof. J. J. B. V. BORDET (Physiology and Medicine, 1919); Prof. N. BOHR (Physics, 1922); Prof. A. V. HILL, C.H., O.B.E. (Physiology and Medicine, 1922); Prof. K. M. G. SIEGBAHN (Physics, 1924); Prof. T. SVEDBERG (Chemistry, 1926); Prince Louis de BROGLIE (Physics, 1929); Prof. O. H. WARBURG (Physiology and Medicine, 1931); Prof. W. HEISENBERG (Physics, 1932); Lord ADRIAN, O.M. (Physiology and Medicine, 1932); Prof. E. SCHRÖDINGER (Physics, 1933); Prof. P. A. M. DIRAC (Physics, 1933).

Sir J. CHADWICK (Physics, 1935); Prof. P. J. W. DEBYE (Chemistry, 1936); Sir H. DALE, O.M., G.B.E. (Physiology and Medicine, 1936); Prof. O. LOEWI (Physiology and Medicine, 1936); Sir G. THOMSON (Physics, 1937); Prof. P. KARRER (Chemistry, 1937); Prof. G. DOMAGK (Physiology and Medicine, 1939); Prof. L. RUZICKA (Chemistry, 1939); Prof. G. C. DE HEVESEY (Chemistry, 1943); Prof. O. HAHN (Chemistry, 1944); Dr. H. S. GASSER (Physiology and Medicine, 1944); Sir H. FLOREY (Physiology and Medicine, 1945); Prof. E. B. CHAIN (Physiology and Medicine, 1945); Prof. P. W. BRIDGMAN (Physics, 1946); Prof. H. J. MULLER (Physiology and Medicine, 1946); Sir E. APPLETON, G.B.E., K.C.B. (Physics, 1947); Sir R. ROBINSON, O.M. (Chemistry, 1947); Prof. C. F. CORI (Physiology and Medicine, 1947); Prof. B. A. HOUSSAY (Physiology and Medicine, 1947); Prof. A. W. K. TISELIUS (Chemistry, 1948); Prof. P. M. S. BLACKETT (Physics, 1948); Prof. C. F. POWELL (Physics, 1950); Prof. T. REICHSTEIN (Physiology and Medicine, 1950); Sir J. COCKCROFT, O.M., K.C.B., C.B.E. (Physics, 1951).

Dr. A. J. P. MARTIN (Chemistry, 1952); Dr. R. L. M. SYNGE (Chemistry, 1952); Prof. F. ZERNIKE (Physics, 1953); Sir H. KREBS (Physiology and Medicine, 1953); Sir W. CHURCHILL (Literature, 1953); Prof. M. BORN (Physics, 1954); Prof. L. C. PAULING (Chemistry, 1954); Prof. A. H. T. THEORELL (Physiology and Medicine, 1955); Sir C. HINSHELWOOD, O.M. (Chemistry, 1956); Academician N. M. SEMENOV (Chemistry, 1956); Sir A. TODD (Chemistry, 1957); Dr. F. SANGER (Chemistry, 1958).

PROGRAMME OF CELEBRATIONS

TUESDAY, JULY 19, 1960

3.30 p.m.: Formal opening by the Queen, accompanied by King Gustav VI Adolf of Sweden and the Duke of Edinburgh, at the Royal Albert Hall. Followed by the Tercentenary Address by the President of the Royal Society, Sir Cyril Hinshelwood.

WEDNESDAY, JULY 20

10.15 a.m.: Tercentenary lectures:
" Chromosomes and the Theory of Heredity " by Professor C. D. Darlington.
" The Evolution of Nuclear Power Plant Design " by Sir Christopher Hinton, K.B.E.
" The Problems of Transplantation " by Professor P. B. Medawar, C.B.E.
2.30 p.m.: Lectures:
" The Physics and Chemistry of Nervous Conduction " by Professor A. L. Hodgkin.
" The Study of Nuclear Interaction at Very Great Energies " by Professor C. F. Powell.
" New Horizons in Organic Chemistry " by Sir Alexander Todd.
8.30 p.m.: Reception by the University of London in the Senate House.

THURSDAY, JULY 21

Included in the events of the day is a trip to Oxford University, with luncheons in the colleges, an Honorary Degree Ceremony at the University, and a garden party at Wadham College.

FRIDAY, JULY 22

11 a.m.: University of London Honorary Degree Ceremony; degrees conferred by the Chancellor of the University, Queen Elizabeth the Queen Mother.
3 p.m.: Premiere at the Royal Festival Hall of films made for the Tercentenary by Shell International.

194

8.15 p.m.: Evening receptions in the City of London, given by the Lord Mayor and Corporation at Guildhall, and by the 12 great City Companies in the Hall of the Mercers' Company.

SATURDAY, JULY 23

10.15 a.m.: Lectures:
" Molecules in Crystals " by Dr. Dorothy Hodgkin.
" The Investigation of the Universe by Radio Astronomy " by Professor A. C. B. Lovell, O.B.E.
" The Metamorphosis of Insects " by Professor V. B. Wigglesworth, C.B.E.
8.30 p.m.: Conversazione by the Royal Society at Burlington House.

SUNDAY, JULY 24

10.30 a.m.: Service at St. Pauls' Cathedral, including a special sermon related to Sir Christopher Wren, by the Dean, the Very Rev. W. R. Matthews.
Seats reserved for an opera at Glyndebourne Festival Opera, Sussex, in the evening.

MONDAY, JULY 25

10.15.: Lecture: " Trends in Aeronautical Science and Engineering " by Sir Arnold Hall.
Further day excursions, the most important being to Cambridge University.
Luncheon in the colleges and garden parties at Trinity and St. John's Colleges.

TUESDAY, JULY 26

Visits to research laboratories in and near London.
Tercentenary celebrations close with a banquet at Grosvenor House.

Other events include visits to many places of interest in London and the provinces, with alternatives for ladies not wishing to take part in the main programme of events—whole-day excursions to Canterbury (with a visit to Down House *en route*), Greenwich Palace and St. Albans; morning visits to the London Stock Exchange, Westminster Abbey, the Houses of Parliament and other places of interest in London; and a fashion display by Courtaulds and British Nylon Spinners.